# Touchstones 1

# NEW SCHOOL SERIES

Consulting Editor:     R. Stone, M.A., A.Inst.P.,
*Second Master, Manchester Grammar School*

General Editor (Arts): B. A. Phythian, M.A., B.Litt.,
*Headmaster, Langley Park School for Boys, Beckenham, Kent*

## Le Français d'Aujourd'hui
Parts One, Two and Three
Pupils' Book, Teacher's Handbook, Audio
Visual Course
Part Four (G.C.E.)
Pupils' Book, Audio Course
P. J. Downes, M.A.
E. A. Griffith, B.A.
Part Four (C.S.E.)
Pupils' Book, Teacher's
Booklet, Audio Course
P. B. Houldsworth, B.A., Doct. de l' Univ. (Paris)

## Starting-Points
Creative Writing for Junior Forms
G. P. Fox, M.A.
B. A. Phythian, M.A., B.Litt.

## Listen
An Anthology of Dramatic Monologues
W. A. Thompson, M.A.

## Creeds and Controversies
A General Studies Book on the
Nature of Religious Belief
P. F. Miller, M.A.
K. S. Pound, M.A.

# Touchstones 1

A TEACHING ANTHOLOGY

M. G. BENTON M.A.
*Lecturer, School of Education, University of Southampton*

P. BENTON M.A.
*Head of English, The Grammar School, Letchworth*

THE ENGLISH UNIVERSITIES PRESS LTD

# Contents

To the Teacher            viii

Creative Writing            x

## PART A

WORD PICTURES
Includes:

| | | |
|---|---|---|
| *Full Moon* | Kikaku | 2 |
| *Summer Night* | Shiki | 3 |
| *In the House* | Issa | 3 |
| *Parting* | Buson | 3 |
| *The Little Duck* | Joso | 4 |

COMPARISONS
Includes:

| | | |
|---|---|---|
| *In the Moonlight* | Shiki | 5 |
| *The Barleyfield* | Sora | 5 |
| *Cynddylan on a Tractor* | R. S. Thomas | 9 |

BALLADS
Includes:

| | | |
|---|---|---|
| *The Twa Sisters* | Anon | 13 |
| *The Twa Corbies* | Anon | 15 |

## PART B

WORD-PICTURES AND COMPARISONS

| | | |
|---|---|---|
| *Above the Dock* | T. E. Hulme | 20 |
| *Coolness in Summer* | Ryusui | 20 |
| *Moon Magic* | Sodo | 20 |
| *Moonlit Apples* | J. Drinkwater | 21 |
| *Moon Viewing* | Hokushi | 22 |
| *The Harvest Moon* | Basho | 22 |
| *Dawn* | Onitsura | 22 |
| *Haze* | Buson | 22 |
| *Heat* | Shiki | 23 |
| *Elephants in the Circus* | D. H. Lawrence | 23 |

| | | |
|---|---|---|
| Song | P. B. Shelley | 23 |
| Crow | Basho | 23 |
| Spring | Ryota | 26 |
| The World Upside Down | Onitsura | 26 |
| Last Snow | Andrew Young | 26 |
| Thaw | Edward Thomas | 27 |
| The Rainbow | D. H. Lawrence | 27 |
| Talk | D. H. Lawrence | 27 |
| The Fountains | W. R. Rodgers | 28 |
| Quiet | Richard Church | 28 |
| Spray | D. H. Lawrence | 29 |
| Autumn | T. E. Hulme | 29 |
| Winter | L. A. G. Strong | 29 |
| Under the Mountain | Louis MacNeice | 30 |
| Cinquains | A. Crapsey | 31 |
| The Fly | Walter de la Mare | 32 |
| Creative Writing | | 33 |

BALLADS

| | | |
|---|---|---|
| The Demon Lover | Anon | 34 |
| The Unquiet Grave | Anon | 36 |
| Sir Patrick Spens | Anon | 37 |
| The Farmer's Curst Wife | Anon | 39 |
| Johnny Sands | Anon | 40 |
| Hanging Johnny | Anon | 41 |
| The Cherry Tree Carol | Anon | 42 |
| Mother and Maiden | Anon | 43 |
| Sea Shanty | Anon | 44 |
| The Dying Cowboy | Anon | 45 |

NARRATIVE

| | | |
|---|---|---|
| From Reynard the Fox | John Masefield | 46 |
| The History of the Flood | John Heath-Stubbs | 50 |
| John Barleycorn | Robert Burns | 54 |
| The Diverting History of John Gilpin | William Cowper | 56 |
| The Yarn of the Nancy Bell | W. S. Gilbert | 65 |

ANIMALS, BIRDS AND INSECTS

| | | |
|---|---|---|
| Bat | D. H. Lawrence | 69 |
| The Swallows | Andrew Young | 71 |
| The Eagle | Lord Tennyson | 72 |
| The Eagle | Andrew Young | 72 |
| The Bird-Fancier | James Kirkup | 73 |
| The Cat and the Moon | W. B. Yeats | 74 |
| Milk for the Cat | Harold Monro | 76 |

| The Moth | Walter de la Mare | 77 |
| The Bells of Heaven | Ralph Hodgson | 78 |
| The Tigress | Clifford Dyment | 78 |
| A Dead Mole | Andrew Young | 80 |
| The Sloth | Theodore Roethke | 80 |
| Diary of a Church Mouse | John Betjeman | 81 |
| The Gallows | Edward Thomas | 83 |
| Ducks | F. W. Harvey | 84 |
| Creative Writing | | 87 |

CITY

| The Excavation | Max Endicoff | 88 |
| Prelude | T. S. Eliot | 90 |
| Westminster Bridge | William Wordsworth | 90 |
| The Seal | Richard Church | 92 |
| Snow in the Suburbs | Thomas Hardy | 93 |
| London Snow | Robert Bridges | 93 |
| Morning Express | Siegfried Sassoon | 95 |
| Creative Writing | | 98 |

COUNTRYSIDE

| The Lonely Scarecrow | James Kirkup | 99 |
| Tall Nettles | Edward Thomas | 102 |
| Weathers | Thomas Harvey | 102 |
| Mid-Country Blows | Theodore Roethke | 103 |
| Cows | James Kirkup | 103 |
| An Autumn Morning | John Clare | 104 |
| The Pettichap's Nest | John Clare | 105 |
| Clearing at Dawn | Li Po (trans. Arthur Waley) | 106 |
| Winter the Huntsman | Osbert Sitwell | 107 |
| Housing Scheme | Richard Church | 108 |
| Creative Writing | | 109 |

HUMOUR

| Mr. Kartoffel | James Reeves | 111 |
| The Tale of Custard the Dragon | Ogden Nash | 112 |
| Growltiger's Last Stand | T. S. Eliot | 114 |
| Macavity the Mystery Cat | T. S. Eliot | 116 |
| The Common Cormorant | Anon | 118 |
| The Walrus and the Carpenter | Lewis Carroll | 119 |
| The Dong with a Luminous Nose | Edward Lear | 122 |
| The Owl and the Pussy-Cat | Edward Lear | 126 |
| Soldier Freddy | Spike Milligan | 127 |

SEA

| Across the Estuary (Part 1) | Norman Nicholson | 128 |
| Full Fathom Five | W. Shakespeare | 129 |

| | | |
|---|---|---|
| *Drowning* | W. Shakespeare | 129 |
| *The Main-Deep* | James Stephens | 130 |
| *Cargoes* | John Masefield | 130 |
| *The Shell* | Lord Tennyson | 131 |
| *The Shell* | James Stephens | 132 |
| *Seaside Serenade* | Ogden Nash | 133 |
| *The* Revenge | Lord Tennyson | 137 |
| Creative Writing | | 142 |

PEOPLE

| | | |
|---|---|---|
| *Children's Party* | Ogden Nash | 143 |
| *Ozymandias* | P. B. Shelley | 144 |
| *Childhood* | Frances Cornford | 145 |
| *The Mad Woman* | L. A. G. Strong | 145 |
| *Zeke* | L. A. G. Strong | 147 |
| *The Old Men Admiring Themselves in the Water* | W. B. Yeats | 147 |
| *Seven Ages of Man* | W. Shakespeare | 148 |
| *The Miller* | Geoffrey Chaucer | 150 |
| Creative Writing | | 153 |

PLACES

| | | |
|---|---|---|
| *Adlestrop* | Edward Thomas | 154 |
| *At the Edge of the Wood* | Peter Redgrove | 155 |
| *Stopping by Woods on a Snowy Evening* | Robert Frost | 155 |
| *The Way Through the Woods* | Rudyard Kipling | 156 |
| *Child on Top of a Greenhouse* | Theodore Roethke | 158 |
| *The Midnight Skaters* | Edmund Blunden | 158 |
| *The Big Rock Candy Mountains* | Anon | 159 |
| Creative Writing | | 161 |

WITCHCRAFT, MAGIC AND MYSTERY

| | | |
|---|---|---|
| *Now the Hungry Lion Roars* | W. Shakespeare | 163 |
| *The Witches' Chant* | W. Shakespeare | 164 |
| *Charm* | Ben Jonson | 165 |
| *Welsh Incident* | R. Graves | 166 |
| *The Listeners* | Walter de la Mare | 167 |
| *Flannan Isle* | Wilfrid Wilson Gibson | 169 |
| *Night Crow* | Theodore Roethke | 172 |
| *Fairies' Song* | W. Shakespeare | 173 |
| *The Knowledgeable Child* | L. A. G. Strong | 174 |
| Creative Writing | | 175 |
| Index of First Lines | | 176 |
| Index of Authors | | 179 |
| Sources and Acknowledgements | | 180 |

# To the Teacher

The idea of 'teaching poetry'—certainly if the phrase is used in any formal, pedagogic sense—is, in itself, suspect: why, therefore, have we compiled a 'teaching anthology'? Briefly, we felt that there was a need for an anthology which offered more than a collection of poems. Poetry lessons depend so much for their success upon a sympathetic relationship between teacher and pupils and, although books will not in themselves create this relationship, they can help considerably by suggesting ideas for discussion, by showing different approaches to poems, and by encouraging pupils to write poetry themselves. We have attempted to satisfy these needs while avoiding the danger of setting out too rigid a procedure. We hope, too, that the teaching material we include will provide some useful starting-points for teachers looking for fresh ideas.

The pattern of our 'teaching anthology' is as follows. First, in Part A, we introduce three main topics which give information about a particular aspect of poetry, illustrate by examples, point questions and provoke discussion. The individual teacher is the best judge of just how and when to use this area of the book. Secondly, in Part B, we have grouped the material so that the teacher will be able to deal with several poems, linked by some common quality of technique, subject matter, style or attitude, in any one lesson or sequence of lessons. Thirdly, at the end of most sections in Part B, we have provided a number of suggestions for encouraging the pupils to write their own poems, in the belief that it is just as important to get a child to write poetry as it is to encourage him to appreciate and criticise. We consider that it is vital that pupils should be allowed the chance to write, to experiment, to play with words and sounds, even with the shapes of poems in the same way that they are allowed free expression with paints and plastic materials in an art lesson. Through this kind of personal involvement comes an understanding and appreciation of what they read and, above all, an understanding of themselves and the world around them.

Although we do suggest certain lines of thought, we do not wish the books to be followed slavishly as a 'course'. Indeed, the distinction between material suited, for example, to a second as opposed to a first form must sometimes be arbitrary. Although we have numbered our books one to five and have chosen our topics and poems to suit particular age-groups, the teacher will find sufficient flexibility in the arrangement to be able to select and modify the material we print according to his own tastes and the abilities of his pupils.

# Creative Writing

There are many ways of stimulating children's writing and every teacher has his own methods. We therefore feel it would be presumptuous to give too much direction and we have in the main limited ourselves to suggestions in the creative writing sections. Whilst we do not positively discourage rhymed verse it is our experience that free verse is the medium best suited to composition at this age. Seeking the correct rhyme and manipulating the words to produce it often kill the original spontaneity and feeling. Free verse enables the child to say what he feels and means and to use the full range of his imagination without being cramped. The approaches to creative writing suggested by M. Langdon* and Sybil Marshall† have, in our experience, worked well and we would encourage teachers using our books to experiment along similar lines with our suggestions for writing poetry. We have indicated in detail on p. 87, using D. H. Lawrence's *Bat*, and on p. 109, where we ask pupils to write about a storm in the countryside, two possible approaches which could be equally well employed with most of the other subjects we include. To go into such detail with all the topics we suggest would clearly be beyond the scope of this book and would encroach upon the freedom of the teacher. A final word: poems cannot be written on demand and we would emphasise that in using the Creative Writing sections teachers should encourage discussion of our suggestions and not present them to the class as 'exercises' which must be completed.

M.G.B.
P.B.

\* Langdon, M. *Let The Children Write: An Explanation Of Intensive Writing* (Longmans)
† Marshall, S. *An Experiment In Education* (C.U.P.)

# PART A

# WORD-PICTURES

Making a picture with words, like doing a jig-saw puzzle, is often not so easy as it looks at first. We all think that we can describe things clearly and vividly enough—after all, we are doing it in conversation every day—but as soon as we try to describe something in writing the right words slip out of place and refuse to convey the picture we want from them. Whether we want to describe a picture in our mind's eye, or a feeling about something, or both, it seems difficult to give the shape of the idea in our heads the same 'shape' in words.

One type of word-picture which tries to overcome this difficulty by being brief and precise is the Japanese Haiku poem. As you will see from the following examples Haiku poems are short, three-line poems which, because of their shortness, cannot afford a lot of detail; what detail there is has to be significant and important to the description.* The Haiku poet has to choose his words with great care because he is using so few; his poems may suggest a scene or incident, they may create an atmosphere, they may express a person's feelings, or they may do several of these things simultaneously.

Here are two Haiku† poems which create a picture:

## Full Moon

Bright the full moon shines:
on the matting of the floor,
shadows of the pines.

---

* In the original Japanese, Haiku do not have rhyme and are usually seventeen-syllable poems, the syllables being arranged 5, 7, 5 on the three lines: in translation, however, it is not always possible to keep to this syllable pattern and often the translator has chosen to make the first and third lines rhyme. But these technical matters are not important at this stage.

† All Haiku in this volume are translations by Harold G. Henderson in his book *An Introduction to Haiku* (Doubleday Anchor, New York 1958).

2

# Summer Night

A lightning flash:
between the forest trees
I have seen water.

As you see, these are clear, simple word-pictures in which the writer concentrates on one central object or scene and leaves the reader to fill in the details of the landscape from his own imagination.

What other details of the picture do you see in your 'mind's eye' when you read each of these poems?
Describe the scene in each poem in your own words and see what details you add.

However, the picture is only one feature of Haiku: frequently these poems will also express a feeling. Here are three more examples:

# In the House

At the butterflies
the caged bird gazes, envying —
just watch its eyes!

# Parting

For me who go,
for you who stay —
two autumns.

# The Little Duck

'I've just come from a place
at the lake bottom!' —*that* is the look
on the little duck's face.

What feelings do these poems suggest in addition to giving us a word-picture?

What are the feelings of the caged bird? Why does the poet refer to its eyes?

In *Parting* what is the feeling expressed by the phrase 'two autumns'?

In the third poem *what* is the look on the duck's face? What does its supposed remark on surfacing tell us about how it feels?

It is quite possible that each member of the class may find something different in these poems for, because Haiku suggest a lot and state so little, there will often be several impressions created in readers' minds. This, of course, goes some way to explaining why one person may like a particular poem while another can see little in it.

# COMPARISONS

Another thing we can learn from Haiku about poems is the usefulness of comparing things. Frequently, in order to overcome the problem we started with — that of telling others about things we have seen, experiences we have had, or emotions we have felt — we turn to comparison. We say something is 'like' something else: that white, fluffy clouds are like candyfloss. Or we assume the idea of 'likeness' and talk about one thing, say rain, in language from another context, for example — the rain 'danced' on the pavement. In both examples there is a comparison of two things because they have some common quality — whiteness and fluffiness in the first, quick continuous movements in the second. You will see what we mean if you look at these two Haiku poems:

## In the Moonlight

It looks like a man,
the scarecrow in the moonlit night —
and it is pitiful.

## The Barleyfield

Up the barley rows,
stitching, stitching them together,
a butterfly goes.

The first poem makes a direct comparison: the scarecrow is like a man. The second poem assumes the comparison of the bobbing movement of the butterfly to be similar to the movement of someone stitching.

You may know these two types of comparison already as simile and metaphor; but whatever sort of comparison is being made the main thing to notice is that comparisons can make poems vivid and more exciting because not only do they help the poet to say more exactly what he means, but they also make both the poet and the reader use their imagination.

We have used the term 'word-picture' a good deal and here you can see how appropriate it is to describe poems like these which are similar to sketches or drawings. In fact the Haiku writer is doing in words what the artist is doing in the picture on pp. 6 and 7, which is also Japanese in origin. Look at the details of the picture carefully:

What is the object behind the raised prow in the background of the picture? A mountain or another wave?
What does the falling spray remind you of?
What does the foaming crest of the wave look like?

In answering these questions you will find yourself using your imagination and trying to think of comparisons. Now try to write a Haiku of your own about this great wave in which you make use of one of these comparisons.

Imagination is difficult to define but we go some way towards it if we say that it is being able to look at things in a fresh or original way. Comparison helps the poet to do this, for he puts together two things which we do not normally connect and gives us a new and vivid picture of them. Dylan Thomas, for example, describes milk-churns standing at the corner of the village street 'like short, silver policemen'. D. H. Lawrence sees bats flying in the evening air as 'bits of old umbrella'. Robert Frost sees delicate, overhanging birch-trees

> '. . . trailing their leaves on the ground
> Like girls on hands and knees that throw their hair
> Before them over their heads to dry in the sun.'

All these comparisons allow us to see the thing being described more clearly. How much more imaginative are they than those worn-out old pictures which were themselves once new but have long since lost their original force through over-use — 'as white as snow', 'raining cats and dogs' — and so on.

Now look at these two verses from *Under the Mountain*★:

★ The complete poem is printed on p. 30.

Seen from above
The foam in the curving bay is a goose-quill
That feathers ... unfeathers ... itself.

Seen from above
The field is a flap and the haycocks buttons
To keep it flush with the earth.

The first verse describes the sea lapping up the beach, the second describes a field.

Where do you imagine the poet is when he describes these scenes?
What is a goose-quill? What does it have in common with the bay?
Why does the poet repeat the word 'feathers' in the last line of verse 1?
What is a 'haycock'?
What is the field dotted with haycocks compared to?

R. S. Thomas's poem *Cynddylan on a Tractor* tells us about a Welsh farmer's first venture into the modern age—the purchase of a tractor. The poem makes frequent use of direct comparison.

# Cynddylan on a Tractor

Ah, you should see Cynddylan on a tractor.
Gone the old look that yoked him to the soil;
He's a new man now, part of the machine,
His nerves of metal and his blood oil.
The clutch curses, but the gears obey
His least bidding, and lo, he's away
Out of the farmyard, scattering hens.
Riding to work now as a great man should,
He is the knight at arms breaking the fields'
Mirror of silence, emptying the wood
Of foxes and squirrels and bright jays.
The sun comes over the tall trees
Kindling all the hedges, but not for him
Who runs his engine on a different fuel.
And all the birds are singing, bills wide in vain,
As Cynddylan passes proudly up the lane.

9

AGRICOLTVRA

Sí hor mi uedi in carte in bronsi e in marmi
Di che cagion ne fu la mano amisa y chi donarti
uolte uñ tardo n'esempio e se pio, da lodarti in
proste e in uomi da che lo prenato la miera uentiadi
tarti don la testa adorno e tempio

Tu che mirando questa mia pittura hor di graui
stupor cinger ti, senti hor eco ridi e hor uggo
dilenti di saper la cagioni di tal figura sappi che
io presi allhor forma e misura e hebbe principio
di freddi y e i toeenti pernieter sine a dolorosi dilenti
di quei che prima menar uita siura

Angelo saluadori form.

Why is Cynddylan described as 'yoked' to the soil?
Which comparisons show that he is 'part of the machine'?
Why is Cynddylan described as a 'knight at arms'?
Which comparison tells us that the quiet morning is shattered by the noise of the tractor?
What does the word 'kindling' suggest about the early-morning sun?

Sometimes painters use a kind of comparison when they *personify* an idea. What do you think is meant by this word? In the picture on p. 10 by Arcimboldo you will see how he has represented Agriculture as a man made up of all kinds of farm implements. Some of them are obviously ancient and not in use today. How many of them can you recognise?

You could draw a picture using the same idea, perhaps of a school-teacher made up of different things associated with school—chalk, rulers, books, pencils and so on — or perhaps a gardener, an electrician, a plumber, a builder, an angler or a carpenter. There are many possibilities. When you have drawn your picture you could write about the character you have created.

# BALLADS

The ballad style of poetry is very different from that of the condensed Haiku poems which we looked at earlier. Ballads, as you probably know, set out to tell a story and sometimes they do so at great length; some of the Robin Hood ballads which were very popular during the fifteenth century have more than ninety verses. The word 'popular' tells us something very important about the ballads; they were composed and enjoyed by all classes of people. They were what is called 'folk-art', and many of the old ballads are known to us today as 'folk-songs'. The word 'song' is also important for it tells us that the ballads have a strong connection with music. They were composed not simply as poems to be read but as songs which could be sung or danced to or even worked to.

Although there were professional ballad makers and singers, the author of a ballad might be almost anyone—a farmer, an innkeeper, a shepherd, a tinker, a travelling pedlar—and he was probably not an author as we use the word for he would not write his story down. He would remember it and perhaps change the story very slightly each time he told it. New verses would be added, unsuccessful verses would drop out. People who heard the song would perhaps remember parts of it and add their own words to fill in the gaps. They might even add bits from a ballad they already knew and so a different version would be born. People who work at repetitive tasks often sing to pass the time and to take their minds off the monotony of the job. This is as true today as it was in medieval England where such tasks as spinning and weaving, grinding and mowing, ploughing the fields and rocking the cradle were all part of the daily routine. An example of this kind of ballad is one which you are sure to know—*One Man Went to Mow*. Apart from these there are those ballad songs composed and sung by sailors to help them keep time in tasks such as hauling up the anchor and setting the sails. *Hanging Johnny* (p. 41) is a work ballad of this type. Do you know any others? What is the special name given to sailors' work songs?

The work ballad has been taken up and developed by various groups in more recent years, particularly in the U.S.A. Working at hard and sometimes lonely jobs, the negro slaves, the convicts on the chain-gangs, the cowboys, the railroad builders and the lumber men all made their contribution to the ballad.

When we think of the old ballad makers we probably think first of the wandering minstrel and the harpist employed by a great lord, both of whom did much to help the spread of ballads. They would sing or recite their poems to a harp accompaniment emphasising dramatic points in their story by striking thrilling chords on the instrument. Such a singer is referred to in this old ballad about two sisters, the daughters of a king. It is Scottish in origin and there are some words that you may find difficult: there are notes to help you:

# The Twa Sisters

There were twa sisters in a bower,
There were twa sisters in a bower,
There were twa sisters in a bower,
There came a knight to be their wooer.

He courted the eldest with glove and ring,
But he loved the youngest above all thing,
He courted the eldest with brooch and knife,
But loved the youngest as his life.

The eldest she was vexed sair,✧        *sore*
And much envied her sister fair.
Into her bower she could not rest,
With grief and spite she almost burst.

Upon a morning fair and clear,
She cried unto her sister dear, ·
'O sister, come to yon sea strand,
And see our father's ships come to land.'

She's ta'en her by the milk white hand,
And led her down to yon sea strand.
The youngest stood upon a stone,
The eldest came and threw her in.

She took her by the middle sma',
And dashed her bonny back to the jaw,
'O sister, sister, take my hand
And I'll make you heir to all my land.

'O sister, sister, take my middle,
And you'll get my gold and my golden girdle.
O sister, sister, save my life,
And I swear I'll never be no man's wife.'

'Foul fall the hand that I should take,
It robbed me of my earthly mate.
Your cherry cheeks and yellow hair,
Make me go maiden for evermair.'

Sometimes she sank, sometimes she swam,
Until she came to the miller's dam.
And out there came the miller's son
And saw the fair maid swimming in.

'O father, father, draw your dam,
Here's either a mermaid or a swan.'
The miller quickly threw the dam
And there he found a drowned woman.

You could not see her yellow hair
For gold and pearl that were so rare.
You could not see her middle sma'
For golden girdle that was so braw.

You could not see her fingers white
For golden rings that were so gryte.❖      *great*
And by there came a harper fine.
That harpéd to the king at dine.

When he did look that lady upon,
He sighed and made a heavy moan.
He's ta'en three locks of her yellow hair,
And with them strung his harp so fair.

The first tune he did play and sing
Was, 'Farewell, to my father the king'.
The nextin◆ tune that he played syne†      ◆*next*    †*soon*
Was, 'Farewell, to my mother the queen'.

The lasten tune that he played then,
Was, 'Woe to my sister, fair Ellen'.

Notice how the ballad composer has stressed a few significant details
and kept the picture he wants you to imagine bold and simple:

You could not see her fingers white
For golden rings that were so gryte.

What other lines or phrases stand out vividly in this way?

Ballads, as you will see, concentrate on the dramatic points in the story
and any unnecessary detail is left out. Look back at the poem. What
are these main turning points?

Many ballads come from Scotland and the Border country and the
harper mentioned in this story of treachery would probably know this
description of the two crows (twa corbies) chatting about where they
will find their dinner and finally deciding that a newly slain knight
should provide an excellent meal.

# The Twa Corbies

As I was walking all alone,
I heard twa corbies making a moan:
The one unto the other say,
'Where shall we gang and dine today?'

'In behind yon auld fail◈ dyke                          *turf*
I wot there lies a new slain knight;
And nobody kens that he lies there,
But his hawk, his hound and his lady fair.

'His hound is to the hunting gane,
His hawk to fetch the wild fowl hame,
His lady's ta'en another mate,
So we may make our dinner sweet.

'Ye'll sit upon his white hause-bane◈                   *collar-bone*
And I'll pike out his bonny blue een;
And with one lock of his golden hair
We'll theek◈ our nest when it grows bare.              *line*

'Many a one for him makes moan,
But none shall ken where he is gone;
O'er his white bones when they are bare,
The wind shall blow for evermair.'

The sharp, dramatic quality in the picture of the black crows, one on the white breast of the corpse and the other picking out the knight's blue eyes with its cruel beak, can still make us shudder.

What feeling do the last lines of the ballad give us?

'O'er his white bones when they are bare,
The wind shall blow for evermair.'

Tragedy was a main theme of the early ballads and there are many stories of death and disaster. One of the most dramatic of these is the story of *Sir Patrick Spens* which you will find on p. 37. Again we see how the story is told with the greatest economy, avoiding all unnecessary description. What description there is helps the story along and we see how the emphasis is on the action and how the story develops in a series of 'flashes', rather like a film cutting from one place to another.

There is an old saying 'the Devil has all the best tunes', and this is certainly true when we look at the subjects of the ballad makers.

In medieval England there were still many who had a strong belief in magic, and women were frequently executed for practising witchcraft. Alongside the Christian religion the old pagan beliefs still flourished, particularly in the country areas, and many ballads reflect these beliefs. Poems such as *The Demon Lover* on p. 34 and *The Unquiet Grave* on p. 36 deal with a favourite theme of the old ballad makers—the spirit returned from the dead. It is significant that there are so few ballads on Christian subjects but some of these are very beautiful and have sometimes been preserved into the present day as carols. *The Cherry Tree Carol* on p. 42 and *Mother and Maiden* on p. 43 are two of the best.

Towards the end of the 16th century a new kind of ballad developed. Booksellers and printers realised that these poems had great commercial possibilities and soon ballads were printed and sold by the thousand in both town and country. Travelling pedlars and street ballad mongers, like the one in the picture overleaf, made their living by them and, to sell more copies, they concentrated on crime, violence and scandal. For example, as late as 1849 the ballad of Rush's murder sold 2,500,000 copies. What was the new development that put such ballad mongers out of business?

# PART B

# WORD-PICTURES AND COMPARISONS

*In this section you will find a number of Haiku poems together with some longer poems by English writers*

---

## Above the Dock

Above the quiet dock in midnight,
Tangled in the tall mast's corded height,
Hangs the moon. What seemed so far away
Is but a child's balloon, forgotten after play.

T. E. HULME

## Coolness in Summer

In all this cool
is the moon also sleeping?
There, in the pool?

## Moon Magic

Leading me along,
my shadow goes back home
from looking at the moon.

# Moonlit Apples

At the top of the house the apples are laid in rows,
And the skylight lets the moonlight in, and those
Apples are deep-sea apples of green. There goes
A cloud on the moon in the autumn night.

A mouse in the wainscot scratches, and scratches, and then
There is no sound at the top of the house of men
Or mice; and the cloud is blown, and the moon again
Dapples the apples with deep-sea light.

They are lying in rows there, under the gloomy beams;
On the sagging floor; they gather the silver streams
Out of the moon, those moonlight apples of dreams,
And quiet is the steep stair under.

In the corridors under there is nothing but sleep.
And stiller than ever on orchard boughs they keep
Tryst with the moon, and deep is the silence, deep
On moon-washed apples of wonder.

J. DRINKWATER

# Moon Viewing

The moon on the pine:
I keep hanging it—taking it off—
and gazing each time.

# The Harvest Moon

Harvest moon:
around the pond I wander
and the night is gone.

# Dawn

Dawnlight opening:
on the barley leaf tips
the hoarfrost of spring.

# Haze

Morning haze:
as in a painting of a dream,
men go their ways.

# Heat

The summer river:
although there is a bridge, my horse
goes through the water.

# Elephants in the Circus

Elephants in the circus
have aeons of weariness round their eyes.
Yet they sit up
and show vast bellies to the children.

D. H. LAWRENCE

# Song

A widow bird sate mourning for her love
   Upon a wintry bough;
The frozen wind crept on above,
   The freezing stream below.

There was no leaf upon the forest bare,
   No flower upon the ground,
And little motion in the air
   Except the mill-wheel's sound.

P. B. SHELLEY

# Crow

On a withered branch
a crow has settled—
autumn nightfall.

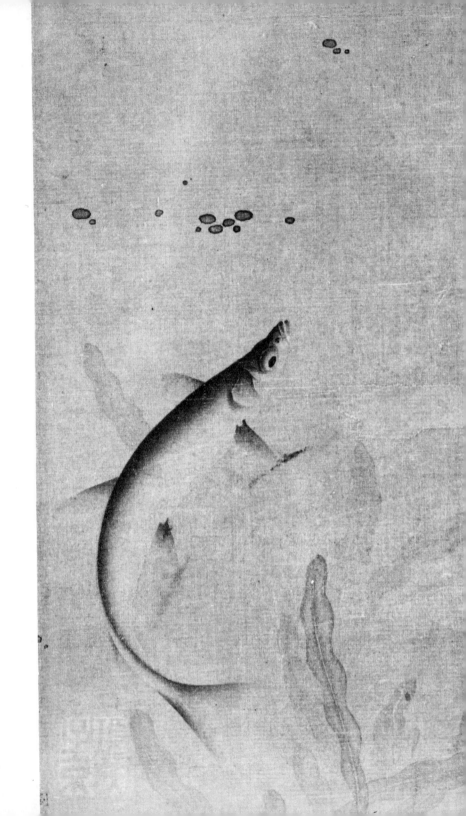

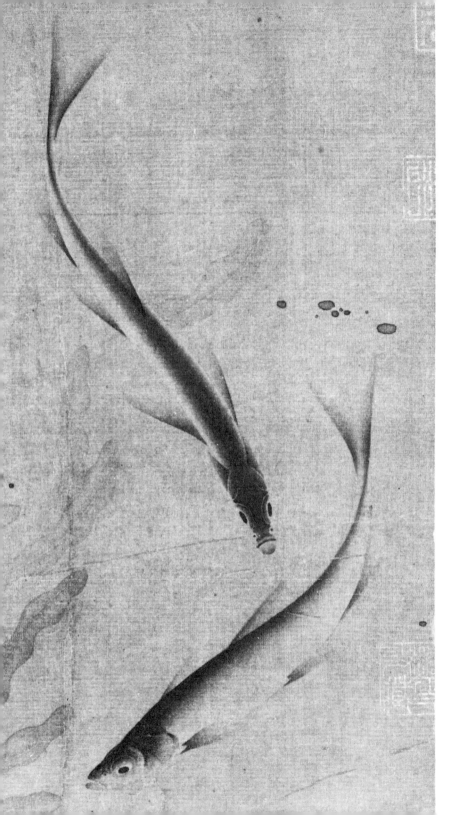

# Spring

They have the guise
of being married just today—
those two butterflies.

# The World Upside Down

A trout leaps high—
below him, in the river bottom,
clouds flow by.

# Last Snow

Although the snow still lingers
Heaped on the ivy's blunt webbed fingers
And painting tree-trunks on one side,
Here in this sunlit ride
The fresh unchristened things appear,
Leaf, spathe and stem,
With crumbs of earth clinging to them
To show the way they came
But no flower yet to tell their name,
And one green spear
Stabbing a dead leaf from below
Kills winter at a blow.

ANDREW YOUNG

# Thaw

Over the land freckled with snow half-thawed
The speculating rooks at their nests cawed
And saw from elm-tops, delicate as flower of grass,
What we below could not see, winter pass.

EDWARD THOMAS

# The Rainbow

Even the rainbow has a body
made of the drizzling rain
and is an architecture of glistening atoms
built up, built up.
yet you can't lay your hand on it,
nay, nor even your mind.

D. H. LAWRENCE

# Talk

I wish people, when you sit near them,
wouldn't think it necessary to make conversation
and send thin draughts of words
blowing down your neck and your ears
and giving you a cold in your inside.

D. H. LAWRENCE

# The Fountains

Suddenly all the fountains in the park
Opened smoothly their umbrellas of water,
Yet there was none but me to miss or mark
Their peacock show, and so I moved away
Uneasily, like one who at play
Finds himself all alone, and will not stay.

W. R. RODGERS

# Quiet

The night was so quiet
That the hum of the candle burning
Came to my ear,
A sound of breath drawn through a reed
Far off.

The night was so quiet
That the air in the room
Poised, waiting to crack
Like a straining
Stick.

The night was so quiet
That the blood and the flesh,
My visible self sunk in the chair,
Was a power-house giant, pulsing
Through the night.

RICHARD CHURCH

# Spray

It is a wonder foam is so beautiful.
A wave bursts in anger on a rock, broken up
in wild white sibilant spray
and falls back, drawing in its breath with rage,
with frustration how beautiful!

D. H. LAWRENCE

# Autumn

A touch of cold in the autumn night—
I walked abroad,
And saw the ruddy moon lean over a hedge,
Like a red-faced farmer.
I did not stop to speak, but nodded,
And round about were the wistful stars
With white faces like town children.

T. E. HULME

# Winter

The winter trees like great sweep's brushes
Poke up from deep earth, black and bare,
Suddenly stir, and shake a crowd
Of sooty rooks into the air.

L. A. G. STRONG

# Under the Mountain

Seen from above
The foam in the curving bay is a goose-quill
That feathers ... unfeathers ... itself.

Seen from above
The field is a flap and the haycocks buttons
To keep it flush with the earth.

Seen from above
The house is a silent gadget whose purpose
Was long since obsolete.

But when you get down
The breakers are cold scum and the wrack
Sizzles with stinking life.

When you get down
The field is a failed or a worth-while crop, the source
Of back-ache if not heart-ache.

And when you get down
The house is a maelstrom of loves and hates where you—
Having got down—belong.

LOUIS MACNEICE

# Cinquains

## TRIAD

These be
Three silent things:
The falling snow ... the hour
Before the dawn ... the mouth of one
Just dead.

## NOVEMBER NIGHT

Listen ...
With faint dry sound,
Like steps of passing ghosts,
The leaves, frost-crisped, break from the trees
And fall.

## THE WARNING

Just now,
Out of the strange
Still dusk ... as strange as still ...
A white moth flew.
Why am I grown so cold?

A. CRAPSEY

# The Fly

How large unto the tiny fly
  Must little things appear!—
A rosebud like a feather bed,
  Its prickle like a spear;


A dewdrop like a looking-glass,
  A hair like golden wire;
The smallest grain of mustard-seed
  As fierce as coals of fire;


A loaf of bread, a lofty hill;
  A wasp, a cruel leopard;
And specks of salt as bright to see
  As lambskins to a shepherd.

WALTER DE LA MARE

# Creative Writing

1 Write down as many different comparisons as you can which are suggested by the following: clouds building up on the horizon; a snowflake; smoke billowing from chimneys; balloons—one or more; tethered or free; the back of your hand; soapsuds; raindrops on a window; frogspawn or tadpoles; frost on a window pane. Discuss these with your teacher. Use one or two of your comparisons as the basis for a short poem.

2 Look again at the Haiku poems on p. 22 and try to write some of your own. You may want to use as models some of the poems we have printed or you may feel confident enough to be original. In either case, remember that your poem will be only three lines long.

The following titles are suggestions; use them if you wish: cranes; the world from space; a willow-tree; flames; loneliness; the cat; still water broken by throwing in a stone or by a fish surfacing; seagulls.

Aim at variety. One Haiku may be a simple picture; another may use a comparison; a third may express a feeling as well as give a picture.

3 Using Louis MacNeice's poem *Under the Mountain* on p. 30 as a model, write your own poem which describes several things from two different points of view. If it helps you can begin the verses in the first part of the poem, 'Seen from above . . .', and, in the second part, 'When you get down . . .'. The following suggestions may help you:

(a) Compare a crowd in the street below with what it is like to be in the crowd.

(b) Describe the wake of a ship as you see it from a cliff-top or from an aeroplane, and then as you think it would look close to.

(c) Above and below the clouds.

(d) Woods seen from above contrasted with what it is like to be walking through them.

(e) A train going through a valley seen from some distance contrasted with the impression it makes when it passes very near you.

4 The three fishes on pages 24 and 25 were painted by a Chinese artist and have something of the neatness, delicacy and balance of a Haiku poem. Perhaps you could write a Haiku about them. Think carefully about their shape and their movement. What are their eyes, their tails and fins like?

33

## The Demon Lover

'O where have you been, my long, long love,
  This long seven years and more?'
'O I'm come to seek my former vows
  Ye granted me before.'

'O hold your tongue of your former vows,
  For they will breed sad strife;
O hold your tongue of your former vows
  For I am become a wife.'

He turned him right and round about,
  And the tear blinded his ee:
'I would never hae trodden on Irish ground,
  If it had not been for thee.

'I might hae had a king's daughter,
  Far, far beyond the sea;
I might have had a king's daughter,
  Had it not been for love o' thee.'

'If ye might have had a king's daughter,
  Yeself ye had to blame;
Ye might have taken the king's daughter,
  For ye kend✦ that I was nane†.          ✦*knew*, †*none*

'If I was to leave my husband dear,
  And my two babes also,
O what have you to take me to,
  If with you I should go?'

'I have seven ships upon the sea—
  And the eighth brought me to land—
With four-and-twenty bold mariners,
  And music on every hand.'

She has taken up her two little babes,
   Kissed them both cheek and chin:
'O fare ye well, my own two babes,
   For I'll never see you again.'

She set her foot upon the ship,
   No mariners could she behold;
But the sails were made of taffeta,
   And the masts of beaten gold.

She had not sailed a league, a league,
   A league but barely three,
When dismal grew his countenance,
   And drumlie❖ grew his ee.†         ❖*gloomy, murky, †eye*

They had not sailed a league, a league,
   A league but barely three,
Until she espied his cloven foot,
   And she wept right bitterly.

'O hold your tongue of your weeping,' says he,
   'Of your weeping now let me be;
I will shew you how the lilies grow
   On the banks of Italy.'

'O what hills are yon, yon pleasant hills,
   That the sun shines sweetly on?'
'O yon are the hills of heaven,' he said,
   'Where you will never win.'

'O whaten❖ a mountain is yon,' she said,      *what sort of*
   'All so dreary with frost and snow?'
'O yon is the mountain of hell,' he cried,
   'Where you and I will go.'

He struck the top-mast with his hand,
   The fore-mast with his knee,
And he broke that gallant ship in twain,
   And sank her in the sea.

# The Unquiet Grave

'The wind doth blow today, my love,
　And a few small drops of rain;
I never had but one true-love,
　In a cold grave she was lain.

'I'll do as much for my true-love
　As any young man may;
I'll sit and mourn all at her grave
　For a twelvemonth and a day.'

The twelvemonth and a day being up,
　The dead began to speak:
'Oh who sits weeping on my grave,
　And will not let me sleep?'

''Tis I, my love, sits on your grave,
　And will not let you sleep;
For I crave one kiss of your clay-cold lips,
　And that is all I seek.'

'You crave one kiss of my clay-cold lips;
　But my breath smells earthy strong;
If you have one kiss of my clay-cold lips,
　Your time will not be long.

''Tis down in yonder garden green,
　Love, where we used to walk,
The finest flower that ere was seen
　Is withered to a stalk.

'The stalk is withered dry, my love,
　So will our hearts decay;
So make yourself content, my love,
　Till God calls you away.'

# Sir Patrick Spens

The king sits in Dunfermline town
  Drinking the blood-red wine:
'O where will I get a good sailor,
  To sail this ship of mine?'

Up and spake an elder knight,
  Sat at the king's right knee:
'Sir Patrick Spens is the best sailor
  That ever sailed the sea.'

The king has written a braid◆ letter          *long*
  And sealed it with his hand.
And sent it to Sir Patrick Spens
  Was walking on the strand.

'To Noroway, to Noroway,
  To Noroway o'er the foam;
The king's own daughter of Noroway,
  'Tis thou must bring her home!'

The first line that Sir Patrick read
  A loud, loud laugh laughed he:
The next line that Sir Patrick read
  The tear blinded his ee◆.          *eye*

'O who is this has done this deed,
  This ill deed unto me;
To send me out this time o' the year
  To sail upon the sea?

37

'Make haste, make haste, my merry men all,
    Our good ship sails the morn.'
'O say not so, my master dear,
    For I fear a deadly storm.

'I saw the new moon late yestere'en
    With the old moon in her arm;
And if we go to sea, master,
    I fear we'll come to harm.'

They had not sailed a league, a league,
    A league, but barely three,
When the sky grew dark, the wind blew loud,
    And angry grew the sea.

The anchor broke, the topmast split,
    'Twas such a deadly storm.
The waves came over the broken ship
    Till all her sides were torn.

O long, long may the ladies sit
    With their fans into their hand,
Or ere they see Sir Patrick Spens
    Come sailing to the strand.

O long, long may the maidens stand
    With their gold combs in their hair,
Before they'll see their own dear loves
    Come home to greet them there.

O forty miles off Aberdeen
    'Tis fifty fathom deep.
And there lies good Sir Patrick Spens
    With the Scots lords at his feet.

# The Farmer's Curst Wife

There was an old farmer in Sussex did dwell,
      (*Whistle refrain*)
There was an old farmer in Sussex did dwell,
And he had a bad wife, as many knew well.
      (*Whistle refrain*)

Then Satan came to the old man at the plough:
'One of your family I must have now.

'It is not your eldest son that I crave,
But it is your old wife, and she I will have.'

'O welcome, good Satan, with all my heart,
I hope you and she will never more part.'

Now Satan has got the old wife on his back,
And he lugged her along, like a pedlar's pack.

He trudged away till they came to his hall-gate;
Says he, 'Here, take in an old Sussex chap's mate.'

O then she did kick the young imps about;
Says one to the other, 'Let's try turn her out.'

She spied thirteen imps all dancing in chains,
She up with her pattens◈ and beat out their brains.   *woodenshoes*

She knocked the old Satan against the wall:
'Let's turn her out, or she'll murder us all.'

Now he's bundled her up on his back amain,◈      *hastily*
And to her old husband he took her again.

'I have been a tormentor the whole of my life,
But I ne'er was tormented so as with your wife.'

# Johnny Sands

A man whose name was Johnny Sands
   Had married Betty Haigh,
And tho' she brought him gold and lands,
   She proved a terrible plague.
For, oh, she was a scolding wife,
   Full of caprice and whim,
He said that he was tired of life,
   And she was tired of him
   And she was tired of him.

Says he, then I will drown myself—
   The river runs below.
Says she, pray do you silly elf,
   I wished it long ago.
Says he, upon the brink I'll stand,
   Do you run down the hill
And push me in with all your might.
   Says she, my love I will
   Says she, my love I will.

For fear that I should courage lack
   And try to save my life,
Pray tie my hands behind my back.
   I will, replied his wife.
She tied them fast as you may think,
   And when securely done,
Now stand, says she, upon the brink,
   And I'll prepare to run
   And I'll prepare to run.

All down the hill his loving bride,
  Now ran with all her force
To push him in—he stepped aside
  And she fell in of course.
Now splashing, dashing, like a fish,
  Oh, save me, Johnny Sands.
I can't my dear, tho' much I wish,
  For you have tied my hands
  For you have tied my hands.

# Hanging Johnny

They call me Hanging Johnny—
  *Away, boys, away!*
They say I hanged a many—
  *Then hang, boys, hang!*

They say I hanged my brother—
  *Away, boys, away!*
They say I hanged my mother—
  *Then hang, boys, hang!*

They say I hanged my Annie—
  *Away, boys, away!*
I hanged her up so canny—
  *Then hang, boys, hang!*

They say I hanged my daddy—
  *Away, boys, away!*
But I never hanged no body—
  *Then hang, boys, hang!*

41

# The Cherry-Tree Carol

Joseph was an old man,
    An old man was he
When he wedded Mary
    In the land of Galilee.

Joseph and Mary walking
    In the midst of a wood
Saw berries and cherries
    As red as the blood.

O then bespoke Mary,
    So meek and so mild,
'Pray get me one cherry,
    For I am with child.'

O then bespoke Joseph,
    So rude and unkind,
'Let him get thee a cherry
    That got thee with child.'

O then bespoke the babe
    Within his mother's womb,
'Bow down, thou tall cherry-tree,
    And give my mother some.'

Then bowed down the tall cherry-tree
    To his mother's right hand,
And she cried, 'See, Joseph,
    I have cherries at command!'

And Mary ate her cherry
    As red as the blood;
Then Mary went on
    With her heavy load.

# Mother and Maiden

I sing of a maiden
   That is matchless.
King of all kings
   For her son she chose.

He came all so still
   Where his mother was,
As dew in April
   That falleth on the grass.

He came all so still
   To his mother's bower,
As dew in April
   That falleth on the flower.

He came all so still—
   There his mother lay,
As dew in April
   That falleth on the spray.

Mother and maiden
   Was never none but she;
Well may such a lady
   God's mother be.

# Sea Shanty

Blow❖ the man down, bullies, blow the man down,  *knock*
  *Way, ay—blow the man down!*
O, blow the man down in Liverpool Town,
  *Give me some time to blow the man down!*

'Twas on a Black Baller I first served my time,
And on that Black Baller I wasted my prime.

'Tis when a Black Baller is clear of the land,
Our boatswain first gives us the word of command.

'Lay aft,' is the cry, 'to the break of the poop,
Or I'll help you along with the toe of my boot!'

Then larboard and starboard on the deck you will sprawl,
For 'Kicking Jack Williams' commands that Black Ball.

'Tis when a Black Baller returns to her dock,
The lassies and lads to the pierhead do flock.

Blow the man down, bullies, blow the man down!
O, blow the man down in Liverpool Town.

As I was walking down Paradise Street,
A brass-bound policeman I happened to meet.

Says he: 'You're a Black-baller by the cut of your hair.
I know you're a Black-baller by the clothes that you wear.'

'O policeman, O policeman, you do me great wrong,
I'm a *Flying Fish* sailor, just home from Hong Kong.'

They gave me three months in Liverpool Town:
For booting and kicking and blowing him down.

44

# The Dying Cowboy

As I walked out in the streets of Laredo,
As I walked out in Laredo one day,
I spied a poor cowboy all wrapped in white linen,
Wrapped up in white linen as cold as the clay.

'I see by your outfit that you are a cowboy,'
These words he did say as I boldly stepped by.
'Come, sit down beside me and hear my sad story;
I was shot in the breast and I know I must die.

Once in my saddle I used to look handsome,
Once in my saddle I used to look gay.
I first went to drinkin' and then to card playin',
Got shot in the breast, which ended my day.

Let sixteen gamblers come handle my coffin,
Let sixteen girls come carry my pall;
Put bunches of roses all over my coffin,
Put roses to deaden the clods as they fall.

And beat the drums slowly and play the fife lowly,
And play the dead march as you carry me along;
Take me to the prairie and lay the sod o'er me,
For I'm a young cowboy and I know I've done wrong.'

We beat the drums slowly and played the fife lowly,
And bitterly wept as we bore him along;
For we all loved our comrade so brave, young and handsome,
We loved the young cowboy although he'd done wrong.

# NARRATIVE

## *From* Reynard the Fox

The pure clean air came sweet to his lungs,
Till he thought foul scorn on those crying tongues.
In a three mile more he would reach the haven
In the Wan Dyke croaked on by the raven.
In a three mile more he would make his berth
On the hard cool floor of a Wan Dyke earth,
Too deep for spade, too curved for terrier,
With the pride of the race to make rest the merrier.
In a three mile more he would reach his dream,
So his game heart gulped and he put on steam.

Like a rocket shot to a ship ashore
The lean red bolt of his body tore,
Like a ripple of wind running swift on grass,
Like a shadow on wheat when a cloud blows past,
Like a turn at the buoy in a cutter sailing
When the bright green gleam lips white at the railing,
Like the April snake whipping back to sheath,
Like the gannet's hurtle on fish beneath,
Like a kestrel chasing, like a sickle reaping,
Like all things swooping, like all things sweeping,
Like a hound for stay, like a stag for swift,
With his shadow beside like spinning drift.

Past the gibbet-stock all stuck with nails,
Where they hanged in chains what had hung at jails,
Past Ashmundshowe where Ashmund sleeps,
And none but the tumbling peewit weeps,
Past Curlew Calling, the gaunt grey corner
Where the curlew comes as a summer mourner,
Past Blowbury Beacon, shaking his fleece,
Where all winds hurry and none brings peace;
Then down on the mile-long green decline,
Where the turf's like spring and the air's like wine,
Where the sweeping spurs of the downland spill
Into Wan Brook Valley and Wan Dyke Hill.

On he went with a galloping rally
Past Maesbury Clump for Wan Brook Valley.
The blood in his veins went romping high,
'Get on, on, on, to the earth or die.'
The air of the downs went purely past
Till he felt the glory of going fast,
Till the terror of death, though there indeed,
Was lulled for a while by his pride of speed.
He was romping away from hounds and hunt,
He had Wan Dyke Hill and his earth in front,
In a one mile more when his point was made
He would rest in safety from dog or spade;
Nose between paws he would hear the shout
Of the 'Gone to earth!' to the hounds without,
The whine of the hounds, and their cat-feet gadding
Scratching the earth and their breath pad-padding;
He would hear the horn call hounds away,
And rest in peace till another day.

In one mile more he would lie at rest,
So for one mile more he would go his best.
He reached the dip at the long droop's end,
And he took what speed he had still to spend.
So down past Maesbury beech-clump grey
That would not be green till the end of May,
Past Arthur's Table, the white chalk boulder,
Where pasque flowers purple the down's grey shoulder,
Past Quichelm's Keeping, past Harry's Thorn,
To Thirty Acre all thin with corn.
As he raced the corn towards Wan Dyke Brook
The pack had view of the way he took;
Robin hallooed from the downland's crest,
He capped them on till they did their best.
The quarter-mile to the Wan Brook's brink
Was raced as quick as a man can think.

And here, as he ran to the huntsman's yelling,
The fox first felt that the pace was telling;
His body and lungs seemed all grown old,
His legs less certain, his heart less bold,
The hound-noise nearer, the hill-slope steeper,
The thud in the blood of his body deeper.
His pride in his speed, his joy in the race,
Were withered away, for what use was pace?
He had run his best, and the hounds ran better,
Then the going worsened, the earth was wetter.
Then his brush drooped down till it sometimes dragged,
And his fur felt sick and his chest was tagged
With taggles of mud, and his pads seemed lead,
It was well for him he'd an earth ahead.

Down he went to the brook and over,
Out of the corn and into the clover,
Over the slope that the Wan Brook drains,

Past Battle Tump where they earthed the Danes,
Then up the hill that the Wan Dyke rings
Where the Sarsen Stones stand grand like kings.
Seven Sarsens of granite grim,
As he ran them by they looked at him;
As he leaped the lip of their earthen paling
The hounds were gaining and he was failing.

He passed the Sarsens, he left the spur,
He pressed uphill to the blasted fir,
He slipped as he leaped the hedge; he slithered.
'He's mine,' thought Robin. 'He's done: he's dithered.'
At the second attempt he cleared the fence,
He turned half-right where the gorse was dense,
He was leading the hounds by a furlong clear.
He was past his best, but his earth was near.
He ran up gorse to the spring of the ramp,
The steep green wall of the dead men's camp,
He sidled up it and scampered down
To the deep green ditch of the Dead Men's Town.

Within, as he reached that soft green turf,
The wind, blowing lonely, moaned like surf,
Desolate ramparts rose up steep
On either side, for the ghosts to keep.
He raced the trench, past the rabbit warren,
Close-grown with moss which the wind made barren;
He passed the spring where the rushes spread,
And there in the stones was his earth ahead.
One last short burst upon failing feet—
There life lay waiting, so sweet, so sweet,
Rest in a darkness, balm for aches.

The earth was stopped. It was barred with stakes.
                              JOHN MASEFIELD

# The History of the Flood

Bang Bang Bang
Said the nails in the Ark.

It's getting rather dark
Said the nails in the Ark.

For the rain is coming down
Said the nails in the Ark.

And you're all like to drown
Said the nails in the Ark.

Dark and black as sin
Said the nails in the Ark

So won't you all come in
Said the nails in the Ark.

But only two by two
Said the nails in the Ark.

So they came in two by two,
The elephant, the kangaroo,
And the gnu,
And the little tiny shrew.

Then the birds
Flocked in like winged words:
Two racket-tailed motmots, two macaws,
Two nuthatches and two
Little bright robins.

And the reptiles: the gila monster, the slow-worm,
The green mamba, the cottonmouth and the alligator—
All squirmed in;
And after a very lengthy walk,
Two giant Galapagos tortoises.

And the insects in their hierarchies:
A queen ant, a king ant, a queen wasp, a king wasp,
A queen bee, a king bee,
And all the beetles, bugs and mosquitoes,
Cascaded in like glittering, murmurous jewels.

But the fish had their wish;
For the rain came down.
People began to drown:
The wicked, the rich—
They gasped out bubbles of pure gold,
Which exhalations
Rose to the constellations.

So for forty days and forty nights
They were on the waste of waters
In those cramped quarters.
It was very dark, damp and lonely.
There was nothing to see, but only
The rain which continued to drop.
It did not stop.

So Noah sent forth a Raven. The raven said 'Kark!
I will not go back to the Ark.'
The raven was footloose,
He fed on the bodies of the rich—
Rich with vitamins and goo.
They had become bloated,
And everywhere they floated.

The raven's heart was black,
He did not come back.

It was not a nice thing to do:
Which is why the raven is a token of wrath,
And creaks like a rusty gate
When he crosses your path; and Fate
Will grant you no luck that day:
The raven is fey:
You were meant to have a scare.
Fortunately in England
The raven is rather rare.

Then Noah sent forth a dove
She did not want to rove.
She longed for her love—
The other turtle dove—
(For her no other dove!)
She brought back a twig from an olive-tree.
There is no more beautiful tree
Anywhere on the earth,
Even when it comes to birth
From six weeks under the sea.

She did not want to rove.
She wanted to take her rest,
And to build herself a nest
All in the olive grove.
She wanted to make love.
She thought that was the best.

The dove was not a rover;
So they knew that the rain was over.
Noah and his wife got out
(They had become rather stout)
And Japhet, Ham and Shem.
(The same could be said of them.)
They looked up at the sky.
The earth was becoming dry.

Then the animals came ashore—
There were more of them than before:
There were two dogs and a litter of puppies;
There were a tom-cat and two tib-cats
And two litters of kittens—cats
Do not obey regulations;
And, as you might expect,
A quantity of rabbits.

God put a rainbow in the sky.
They wondered what it was for.
There had never been a rainbow before.
The rainbow was a sign;
It looked like a neon sign—
Seven colours arched in the skies:
What should it publicize?
They looked up with wondering eyes.

It advertises Mercy
Said the nails in the Ark.

Mercy Mercy Mercy
Said the nails in the Ark.

Our God is merciful
Said the nails in the Ark.

Merciful and gracious
Bang Bang Bang Bang.

JOHN HEATH-STUBBS

# John Barleycorn

There were three kings into the east,
   Three kings both great and high;
And they hae sworn a solemn oath
   John Barleycorn should die.

They took a plough and plough'd him down,
   Put clods upon his head;
And they hae sworn a solemn oath
   John Barleycorn was dead.

But the cheerful Spring came kindly on,
   And show'rs began to fall;
John Barleycorn got up again,
   And sore surpris'd them all.

The sultry suns of Summer came,
   And he grew thick and strong;
His head weel arm'd wi' pointed spears,
   That no one should him wrong.

The sober Autumn enter'd mild,
   When he grew wan and pale;
His bending joints and drooping head
   Show'd he began to fail.

His colour sicken'd more and more,
   He faded into age;
And then his enemies began
   To show their deadly rage.

They've ta'en a weapon, long and sharp,
   And cut him by the knee;
Then tied him fast upon a cart,
   Like a rogue for forgerie.

They laid him down upon his back,
  And cudgell'd him full sore;
They hung him up before the storm,
  And turn'd him o'er and o'er.


They filléd up a darksome pit
  With water to the brim;
They heavéd in John Barleycorn,
  There let him sink or swim.


They laid him out upon the floor,
  To work him further woe:
And still, as signs of life appear'd,
  They toss'd him to and fro.


They wasted o'er a scorching flame
  The marrow of his bones;
But a miller us'd him worst of all—
  He crush'd him 'tween two stones.


And they hae ta'en his very heart's blood,
  And drank it round and round;
And still the more and more they drank,
  Their joy did more abound.


John Barleycorn was a hero bold,
  Of noble enterprise;
For if you do but taste his blood,
  'Twill make your courage rise.


'Twill make a man forget his woe;
  'Twill heighten all his joy;
'Twill make the widow's heart to sing,
  Tho' the tear were in her eye.

Then let us toast John Barleycorn,
   Each man a glass in hand;
And may his great posterity
   Ne'er fail in old Scotland.

ROBERT BURNS

# The Diverting History of John Gilpin

*Showing how he went farther than he intended, and came safe home again*

John Gilpin was a citizen
Of credit and renown,
A train-band captain eke was he
Of famous London town.

John Gilpin's spouse said to her dear—
'Though wedded we have been
These twice ten tedious years, yet we
No holiday have seen.

'To-morrow is our wedding-day,
And we will then repair
Unto the Bell at Edmonton,
All in a chaise and pair.

'My sister, and my sister's child,
Myself, and children three,
Will fill the chaise; so you must ride
On horseback after we.'

He soon replied—'I do admire
Of womankind but one,
And you are she, my dearest dear,
Therefore it shall be done.

'I am a linen-draper bold,
As all the world doth know,
And my good friend the calender◆        *a maker of cloth*
Will lend his horse to go.'

Quoth Mrs. Gilpin—'That's well said;
And, for that wine is dear,
We will be furnished with our own,
Which is both bright and clear.'

John Gilpin kissed his loving wife;
O'erjoyed was he to find
That, though on pleasure she was bent,
She had a frugal mind.

The morning came, the chaise was brought,
But yet was not allowed
To drive up to the door, lest all
Should say that she was proud.

So three doors off the chaise was stayed,
Where they did all get in;
Six precious souls, and all agog
To dash through thick and thin!

Smack went the whip, round went the wheels,
Were never folk so glad,
The stones did rattle underneath,
As if Cheapside were mad.

John Gilpin at his horse's side
Seized fast the flowing mane,
And up he got, in haste to ride,
But soon came down again;

For saddle-tree scarce reached had he,
His journey to begin,
When, turning round his head, he saw
Three customers come in.

So down he came; for loss of time,
Although it grieved him sore,
Yet loss of pence, full well he knew,
Would trouble him much more.

'Twas long before the customers
Were suited to their mind,
When Betty screaming came downstairs—
'The wine is left behind!'

'Good lack!' quoth he—'yet bring it me,
My leathern belt likewise,
In which I bear my trusty sword
When I do exercise.'

Now mistress Gilpin (careful soul!)
Had two stone bottles found,
To hold the liquor that she loved,
And keep it safe and sound.

Each bottle had a curling ear,
Through which the belt he drew,
And hung a bottle on each side,
To make his balance true.

Then, over all, that he might be
Equipped from top to toe,
His long red cloak, well brushed and neat,
He manfully did throw.

Now see him mounted once again
Upon his nimble steed,
Full slowly pacing o'er the stones
With caution and good heed!

But, finding soon a smoother road
Beneath his well-shod feet,
The snorting beast began to trot,
Which galled him in his seat.

So, 'Fair and softly,' John he cried,
But John he cried in vain;
That trot became a gallop soon,
In spite of curb and rein.

So stooping down, as needs he must
Who cannot sit upright,
He grasped the mane with both his hands,
And eke with all his might.

His horse, who never in that sort
Had handled been before,
What thing upon his back had got
Did wonder more and more.

Away went Gilpin, neck or nought;
Away went hat and wig!—
He little dreamt, when he set out,
Of running such a rig!

The wind did blow, the cloak did fly
Like streamer long and gay,
Till, loop and button failing both,
At last it flew away.

Then might all people well discern
The bottles he had slung;
A bottle swinging at each side,
As hath been said or sung.

The dogs did bark, the children screamed,
Up flew the windows all;
And ev'ry soul cried out—'Well done!'
As loud as he could bawl.

Away went Gilpin—who but he?
His fame soon spread around—
'He carries weight!' 'He rides a race!'
''Tis for a thousand pound!'

And still, as fast as he drew near,
'Twas wonderful to view
How in a trice the turnpike-men
Their gates wide open threw.

And now, as he went bowing down
His reeking head full low,
The bottles twain behind his back
Were shattered at a blow.

Down ran the wine into the road,
Most piteous to be seen,
Which made his horse's flanks to smoke
As they had basted been.

But still he seemed to carry weight,
With leathern girdle braced;
For all might see the bottle-necks
Still dangling at his waist.

Thus all through merry Islington
These gambols he did play,
Until he came unto the Wash❖          *a low-lying stretch of land*
Of Edmonton so gay.

And there he threw the wash❖ about      *pools of water lying on*
On both sides of the way,                 *the marshy ground*
Just like unto a trundling mop,
Or a wild goose at play.

At Edmonton his loving wife
From the balcóny spied
Her tender husband, wond'ring much
To see how he did ride.

'Stop, stop, John Gilpin!—Here's the house'—
They all at once did cry;
'The dinner waits, and we are tired.'
Said Gilpin—'So am I!'

But yet his horse was not a whit
Inclined to tarry there;
For why?—his owner had a house
Full ten miles off, at Ware.

So like an arrow swift he flew,
Shot by an archer strong;
So did he fly—which brings me to
The middle of my song.

Away went Gilpin, out of breath,
And sore against his will,
Till at his friend the calender's
His horse at last stood still.

The calender, amazed to see
His neighbour in such trim,
Laid down his pipe, flew to the gate,
And thus accosted him:

'What news? what news? your tidings tell;
Tell me you must and shall—
Say why bare-headed you are come,
Or why you come at all?'

Now Gilpin had a pleasant wit,
And loved a timely joke;
And thus unto the calender
In merry guise he spoke:

'I came because your horse would come;
And, if I well forbode,
My hat and wig will soon be here—
They are upon the road.'

The calender, right glad to find
His friend in merry pin,
Returned him not a single word,
But to the house went in;

Whence straight he came with hat and wig;
A wig that flowed behind,
A hat not much the worse for wear,
Each comely in its kind.

He held them up, and, in his turn,
Thus showed his ready wit—
'My head is twice as big as yours,
They therefore needs must fit.

'But let me scrape the dirt away
That hangs upon your face;
And stop and eat, for well you may
Be in a hungry case.'

Said John—'It is my wedding-day,
And all the world would stare,
If wife should dine at Edmonton
And I should dine at Ware!'

So, turning to his horse, he said—
'I am in haste to dine;
'Twas for your pleasure you came here,
You shall go back for mine.'

Ah, luckless speech, and bootless boast!
For which he paid full dear;
For, while he spake, a braying ass
Did sing most loud and clear;

Whereat his horse did snort, as he
Had heard a lion roar,
And galloped off with all his might,
As he had done before.

Away went Gilpin, and away
Went Gilpin's hat and wig!
He lost them sooner than at first—
For why?—they were too big!

Now, mistress Gilpin, when she saw
Her husband posting down
Into the country far away,
She pulled out half a crown;

And thus unto the youth she said
That drove them to the Bell—
'This shall be yours when you bring back
My husband safe and well.'

The youth did ride, and soon did meet
John coming back amain;
Whom in a trice he tried to stop
By catching at his rein;

But, not performing what he meant,
And gladly would have done,
The frighted steed he frighted more,
And made him faster run.

Away went Gilpin, and away
Went post-boy at his heels!
The post-boy's horse right glad to miss
The lumb'ring of the wheels.

Six gentlemen upon the road,
Thus seeing Gilpin fly,
With post-boy scamp'ring in the rear,
They raised the hue and cry:

'Stop thief! stop thief!—a highwayman!'
Not one of them was mute;
And all and each that passed that way
Did join in the pursuit.

And now the turnpike gates again
Flew open in short space;
The toll-men thinking, as before,
That Gilpin rode a race.

And so he did—and won it too!—
For he got first to town;
Nor stopped till where he had got up
He did again get down.

Now let us sing—Long live the king,
And Gilpin long live he;
And, when he next doth ride abroad,
May I be there to see!

WILLIAM COWPER

# The Yarn of the Nancy Bell

'Twas on the shores that round our coast
  From Deal to Ramsgate span,
That I found alone on a piece of stone
  An elderly naval man.

His hair was weedy, his beard was long,
  And weedy and long was he,
And I heard this wight on the shore recite,
  In a singular minor key:

'Oh, I am a cook and a captain bold,
  And the mate of the *NANCY* brig,
And a bo'sun tight, and a midshipmite,
  And the crew of the captain's gig.'

And he shook his fists and he tore his hair,
    Till I really felt afraid,
For I couldn't help thinking the man had been drinking,
    And so I simply said:


'Oh, elderly man, it's little I know
    Of the duties of men of the sea,
And I'll eat my hand if I understand
    How you can possibly be


At once a cook, and a captain bold,
    And the mate of the *NANCY* brig,
And a bo'sun tight, and a midshipmite,
    And the crew of the captain's gig.'


Then he gave a hitch to his trousers, which
    Is a trick all seamen larn,
And having got rid of a thumping quid,
    He spun his painful yarn:


''Twas in the good ship *NANCY BELL*
    That we sailed to the Indian Sea,
And there on a reef we come to grief,
    Which has often occurred to me.


And pretty nigh all the crew was drowned
    (There was seventy-seven o' soul)
And only ten of the *NANCY's* men
    Said "here" to the muster-roll.


There was me and the cook and the captain bold,
    And the mate of the *NANCY* brig,
And the bo'sun tight, and a midshipmite,
    And the crew of the captain's gig.

For a month we'd neither wittles nor drink,
  Till a-hungry we did feel,
So we drawed a lot, and accordin' shot
  The captain for our meal.

The next lot fell to the NANCY's mate,
  And a delicate dish he made;
Then our appetite with the midshipmite
  We seven survivors stayed.

And then we murdered the bo'sun tight,
  And he much resembled pig;
Then we wittled free, did the cook and me,
  On the crew of the captain's gig.

Then only the cook and me was left,
  And the delicate question, "Which
Of us two goes to the kettle?" arose,
  And we argued it out as sich.

For I loved that cook as a brother, I did,
  And the cook he worshipped me;
But we'd both be blowed if we'd either be stowed
  In the other chap's hold, you see.

"I'll be eat if you dines off me," says Tom.
  "Yes, that," says I, "you'll be,—
I'm boiled if I die, my friend," quoth I.
  And "Exactly so," quoth he.

Says he, "Dear James, to murder me
  Were a foolish thing to do,
For don't you see that you can't cook me,
  While I can—and will—cook you!"

So he boils the water, and takes the salt
  And the pepper in portions true
(Which he never forgot), and some chopped shallott,
  And some sage and parsley too.

"Come here," says he, with a proper pride,
  Which his smiling features tell,
"'Twill soothing be if I let you see
  How extremely nice you'll smell."

And he stirred it round and round and round,
  And he sniffed at the foaming froth;
When I ups with his heels, and smothers his squeals
  In the scum of the boiling broth.

And I eat that cook in a week or less,
  And—as I eating be
The last of his chops, why, I almost drops,
  For a vessel in sight I see.

And I never larf, and I never smile,
  And I never lark or play,
But sit and croak, and a single joke
  I have,—which is to say:

Oh, I am a cook and a captain bold,
  And the mate of the *NANCY* brig,
And a bo'sun tight, and a midshipmite,
  And the crew of the captain's gig.'

                                    W. S. GILBERT

# ANIMALS, BIRDS and INSECTS

## Bat

At evening, sitting on this terrace,
When the sun from the west, beyond Pisa, beyond the
      mountains of Carrara
Departs, and the world is taken by surprise . . .

When the tired flower of Florence is in gloom beneath the
      glowing
Brown hills surrounding . . .
When under the arches of the Ponte Vecchio
A green light enters against stream, flush from the west,
Against the current of obscure Arno . . .

Look up, and you see things flying
Between the day and the night;
Swallows with spools of dark thread sewing the shadows
      together.

A circle swoop, and a quick parabola under the bridge arches
Where light pushes through;
A sudden turning upon itself of a thing in the air.
A dip to the water.

And you think:
'The swallows are flying so late!'

Swallows?

Dark air-life looping
Yet missing the pure loop . . .
A twitch, a twitter, an elastic shudder in flight
And serrated wings against the sky,
Like a glove, a black glove thrown up at the light,
And falling back.

Never swallows!
*Bats!*
The swallows are gone.

At a wavering instant the swallows give way to bats
By the Ponte Vecchio . . .
Changing guard.

Bats, and an uneasy creeping in one's scalp
As the bats swoop overhead!
Flying madly.

Pipistrello!
Black piper on an infinitesimal pipe.
Little lumps that fly in air and have voices indefinite,
        wildly vindictive;

Wings like bits of umbrella.

Bats!

Creatures that hang themselves up like an old rag, to sleep;
And disgustingly upside down.
Hanging upside down like rows of disgusting old rags
And grinning in their sleep.
Bats!

In China the bat is symbol of happiness.

Not for me!

D. H. LAWRENCE

# The Swallows

All day—when early morning shone
With every dewdrop its own dawn
And when cockchafers were abroad
Hurtling like missiles that had lost their road—

The swallows twisting here and there
Round unseen corners in the air
Upstream and down so quickly passed
I wondered that their shadows flew as fast.

They steeple-chased over the bridge
And dropped down to a drowning midge
Sharing the river with the fish,
Although the air itself was their chief dish.

Blue-winged snowballs! until they turned
And then with ruddy breasts they burned;
All in one instant everywhere,
Jugglers with their own bodies in the air.

ANDREW YOUNG

# The Eagle

He clasps the crag with hookéd hands;
Close to the sun in lonely lands,
Ringed with the azure world, he stands.

The wrinkled sea beneath him crawls;
He watches from his mountain walls,
And like a thunderbolt he falls.

LORD TENNYSON

# The Eagle

He hangs between his wings outspread
　　Level and still
And bends a narrow golden head,
　　Scanning the ground to kill.

Yet as he sails and smoothly swings
　　Round the hill-side,
He looks as though from his own wings
　　He hung down crucified.

ANDREW YOUNG

72

# The Bird-Fancier

Up to his shoulders
In grasses coarse as silk,
The white cat with the yellow eyes
Sits with all four paws together,
Tall as a quart of milk.

He hardly moves his head
To touch with nice nose
What his wary whiskers tell him
Is here a weed
And here a rose.

On a dry stick he rubs his jaws,
And the thin
Corners of his smile
Silently mew when a leaf
Tickles his chin.

With a neat grimace
He nips a new
Blade of feathery grass,
Flicks from his ear
A grain of dew.

His sleepy eyes are wild with birds.
Every sparrow, thrush and wren
Widens their furred horizons
Till their flying song
Narrows them again.

JAMES KIRKUP

# The Cat and the Moon

The cat went here and there
And the moon spun round like a top,
And the nearest kin of the moon,
The creeping cat, looked up.
Black Minnaloushe stared at the moon,
For, wander and wail as he would,
The pure cold light in the sky
Troubled his animal blood.
Minnaloushe runs in the grass
Lifting his delicate feet.
Do you dance, Minnaloushe, do you dance?
When two close kindred meet,
What better than call a dance?
Maybe the moon may learn,
Tired of that courtly fashion,
A new dance turn.
Minnaloushe creeps through the grass
From moonlit place to place,
The sacred moon overhead
Has taken a new phase.
Does Minnaloushe know that his pupils
Will pass from change to change,
And that from round to crescent,
From crescent to round they range?
Minnaloushe creeps through the grass
Alone, important and wise,
And lifts to the changing moon
His changing eyes.

W. B. YEATS

# Milk for the Cat

When the tea is brought at five o'clock,
   And all the neat curtains are drawn with care,
The little black cat with bright green eyes
   Is suddenly purring there.

At first she pretends, having nothing to do,
   She has come in merely to blink by the grate,
But, though tea may be late or the milk may be sour,
   She is never late.

And presently her agate eyes
   Take a soft large milky haze,
And her independent casual glance
   Becomes a stiff hard gaze.

Then she stamps her claws or lifts her ears
   Or twists her tail and begins to stir,
Till suddenly all her lithe body becomes
   One breathing trembling purr.

The children eat and wriggle and laugh;
   The two old ladies stroke their silk:
But the cat is grown small and thin with desire,
   Transformed to a creeping lust for milk.

The white saucer like some full moon descends
   At last from the clouds of the table above;
She sighs and dreams and thrills and glows,
   Transfigured with love.

She nestles over the shining rim,
   Buries her chin in the creamy sea;
Her tail hangs loose; each drowsy paw
   Is doubled under each bending knee.

A long dim ecstasy holds her life;
    Her world is an infinite shapeless white,
Till her tongue has curled the last holy drop,
    Then she sinks back into the night.

Draws and dips her body to heap
    Her sleepy nerves in the great arm-chair,
Lies defeated and buried deep
    Three or four hours unconscious there.

HAROLD MONRO

# The Moth

Isled in the midnight air,
Musked with the dark's faint bloom,
Out into glooming and secret haunts
    The flame cries, 'Come!'

Lovely in dye and fan,
A-tremble in shimmering grace,
A moth from her winter swoon
    Uplifts her face:

Stares from her glamorous eyes;
Wafts her on plumes like mist;
In ecstasy swirls and sways
    To her strange tryst.

WALTER DE LA MARE

# The Bells of Heaven

'Twould ring the bells of Heaven
The wildest peal for years,
If Parson lost his senses
And people came to theirs,
And he and they together
Knelt down with angry prayers
For tamed and shabby tigers
And dancing dogs and bears,
And wretched, blind pit ponies,
And little hunted hares.

RALPH HODGSON

# The Tigress

They trapped her in the Indian hills
And put her in a box; and though so young
The dockers quailed to hear her voice
As she made war on every bolt and thong.

Now she paces, sleeps on her ledge,
Glares, growls, excretes, gnaws lumps of meat,
Sun and shadow in iron bars
Dropping about her and a listless mate.

CLIFFORD DYMENT

# A Dead Mole

Strong-shouldered mole,
That so much lived below the ground,
Dug, fought and loved, hunted and fed,
For you to raise a mound
Was as for us to make a hole;
What wonder now that being dead
Your body lies here stout and square
Buried within the blue vault of the air?

ANDREW YOUNG

# The Sloth

In moving-slow he has no Peer.
You ask him something in his ear,
He thinks about it for a year;

And, then, before he says a Word
There, upside down (unlike a Bird),
He will assume that you have Heard —

A most Ex-as-per-at-ing Lug.
But should you call his manner Smug,
He'll sigh and give his Branch a Hug;

Then off again to Sleep he goes,
Still swaying gently by his Toes,
And you just *know* he knows he knows.

THEODORE ROETHKE

# Diary of a Church Mouse

Here among long-discarded cassocks,
Damp stools, and half-split open hassocks,
Here where the Vicar never looks
I nibble through old service books.
Lean and alone I spend my days
Behind this Church of England baize.
I share my dark forgotten room
With two oil-lamps and half a broom.
The cleaner never bothers me,
So here I eat my frugal tea.
My bread is sawdust mixed with straw;
My jam is polish for the floor.
   Christmas and Easter may be feasts
For congregations and for priests,
And so may Whitsun. All the same,
They do not fill my meagre frame.
For me the only feast at all
Is Autumn's Harvest Festival,
When I can satisfy my want
With ears of corn around the font.
I climb the eagle's brazen head
To burrow through a loaf of bread.
I scramble up the pulpit stair
And gnaw the marrows hanging there.
   It is enjoyable to taste
These items ere they go to waste,
But how annoying when one finds
That other mice with pagan minds
Come into church my food to share
Who have no proper business there.
Two field mice who have no desire
To be baptized, invade the choir.
A large and most unfriendly rat
Comes in to see what we are at.

He says he thinks there is no God
And yet he comes ... it's rather odd.
This year he stole a sheaf of wheat
(It screened our special preacher's seat).
And prosperous mice from fields away
Came in to hear the organ play,
And under cover of its notes
Ate through the altar's sheaf of oats.
A Low Church mouse, who thinks that I
Am too papistical, and High,
Yet somehow doesn't think it wrong
To munch through Harvest Evensong,
While I, who starve the whole year through,
Must share my food with rodents who
Except at this time of the year
Not once inside the church appear.
    Within the human world I know
Such goings-on could not be so,
For human beings only do
What their religion tells them to.
They read the Bible every day
And always, night and morning, pray,
And just like me, the good church mouse,
Worship each week in God's own house.
    But all the same it's strange to me
How very full the church can be
With people I don't see at all
Except at Harvest Festival.

JOHN BETJEMAN

# The Gallows

There was a weasel lived in the sun
With all his family,
Till a keeper shot him with his gun
And hung him up on a tree,
Where he swings in the wind and rain,
In the sun and in the snow,
Without pleasure, without pain,
On the dead oak tree bough.

There was a crow who was no sleeper,
But a thief and a murderer
Till a very late hour; and this keeper
Made him one of the things that were,
To hang and flap in rain and wind,
In the sun and in the snow.
There are no more sins to be sinned
On the dead oak tree bough.

There was a magpie, too,
Had a long tongue and a long tail;
He could both talk and do—
But what did that avail?
He, too, flaps in the wind and rain
Alongside weasel and crow,
Without pleasure, without pain,
On the dead oak tree bough.

And many other beasts
And birds, skin, bone, and feather,
Have been taken from their feasts
And hung up there together,
To swing and have endless leisure
In the sun and in the snow,
Without pain, without pleasure,
On the dead oak tree bough.

EDWARD THOMAS

83

# Ducks

I

From troubles of the world
I turn to ducks,
Beautiful comical things
Sleeping or curled
Their heads beneath white wings
By water cool,
Or finding curious things
To eat in various mucks
Beneath the pool,
Tails uppermost, or waddling
Sailor-like on the shores
Of ponds, or paddling
—Left! right!—with fanlike feet
Which are for steady oars
When they (white galleys) float
Each bird a boat
Rippling at will the sweet
Wide waterway . . .
When night is fallen *you* creep
Upstairs, but drakes and dillies
Nest with pale water-stars,
Moonbeams and shadow bars
And water-lilies:
Fearful too much to sleep
Since they've no locks
To click against the teeth
Of weasel and fox.
And warm beneath
Are eggs of cloudy green
When hungry rats and lean
Would stealthily suck
New life, but for the mien,
The bold ferocious mien
Of the mother-duck.

II

Yes, ducks are valiant things
On nests of twigs and straws,
And ducks are soothy things
And lovely on the lake
When that the sunlight draws
Thereon their pictures dim
In colours cool.
And when beneath the pool
They dabble, and when they swim
And make their rippling rings,
O ducks are beautiful things!

But ducks are comical things:
As comical as you.
Quack!
They waddle round, they do.
They eat all sorts of things.
And then they quack.
By barn and stable and stack
They wander at their will,
But if you go too near
They look at you through black
Small topaz-tinted eyes.
And wish you ill.
Triangular and clear
They leave their curious track
In mud at the water's edge,
And there amid the sedge
And slime they gobble and peer
Saying 'Quack! quack!'

III

When God had finished the stars and whirl of coloured suns
He turned His mind from big things to fashion little ones,
Beautiful tiny things (like daisies) He made, and then

He made the comical ones in case the minds of men
  Should stiffen and become
  Dull, humourless and glum:
And so forgetful of their Maker be
As to take even themselves—*quite seriously*.
Caterpillars and cats are lively and excellent puns:
All God's jokes are good—even the practical ones!
And as for the duck, I think God must have smiled a bit
Seeing those eyes blink on the day He fashioned it.
And He's probably laughing still at the sound that came
  out of its bill!

F. W. HARVEY

# Creative Writing

1 Look at D. H. Lawrence's poem *Bat* on p. 69 and see how he arranges his ideas and phrases. Notice the things that Lawrence does and does not do. He does not bother with rhyme; he varies the length of the lines; and he uses comparisons. Discuss with your teacher the reasons why Lawrence chooses to do each of these things.

Now write your own poem in the same style. Jot down some notes. Here are some ideas which may help you to begin. Think of any creature: it may be a pet (if so the picture on p. 75 might help), a farm animal, or a wild one, and write down one or two words or phrases suggested by the following questions:

Where do you imagine your animal to be? Put it in its setting.
Is it moving or still?
What colour is it? Are there any markings on its body?
What would it be like to touch?
Now describe its face. Look especially at its eyes and mouth.
What is its expression? Does this suggest its feelings or thoughts?
What are your feelings about it? Do you imagine that other people regard the animal in the same way? Why?

Now that you have made your notes, remember the three things we noticed about Lawrence's *Bat,* and then write your own poem using your notes.

2 Using Tennyson's *Eagle* on p. 72 as a model, write a poem about any creature. Keep to the six lines, in two groups of three.

3 Think of your last visit to a zoo.

Write about the creature which you found most interesting; or, write a poem suggested by one of the following:
(a) Feeding time in the lions' cage or the seals' pool.
(b) Animals in captivity. (Look again at *Bells of Heaven* and *The Tigress* on p. 78 and at the picture of *Two Chained Monkeys* on p. 79.)

4 Imagine there is a large insect on your exercise book. What is it? A spider? An ear-wig? Write a poem to describe the insect and your feelings about it.

5 Write a poem suggested by one of the following: a bird looking for worms; fledglings in a nest waiting to be fed; the vulture; a swan moving across a lake; an ants' nest.

# The Excavation

Clusters of electric bulbs
Like giant chrysanthemums
Paint the black cavern
With streaks and blots
Of faded yellow.
In grotesque mimicry
The monstrous shadows
Ape each movement of toiling men.
The stale pungent odour of unpacked earth
Tickles the nostrils.
Through the wood-plank roof
The dull-booming rumble
Of scampering traffic
Trickles in—
But is swallowed up
By the harsh purr of the drill
As it bites frenziedly
Into the dogged rock.

Overhead, unseen,
A mountain of stone is kept upright
By a slender steel beam
And a theory.

MAX ENDICOFF

# Prelude

The winter evening settles down
With smell of steaks in passageways.
Six o'clock.
The burnt-out ends of smoky days.
And now a gusty shower wraps
The grimy scraps
Of withered leaves about your feet,
And newspapers from vacant lots;
The showers beat
On broken blinds and chimney-pots,
And at the corner of the street
A lonely cab-horse steams and stamps.
And then the lighting of the lamps.

T. S. ELIOT

# Westminster Bridge

Earth has not anything to show more fair:
Dull would he be of soul who could pass by
A sight so touching in its majesty:
This city now doth, like a garment, wear
The beauty of the morning; silent, bare,
Ships, towers, domes, theatres, and temples lie
Open unto the fields, and to the sky;
All bright and glittering in the smokeless air.
Never did sun more beautifully steep
In his first splendour, valley, rock, or hill;
Ne'er saw I, never felt, a calm so deep!
The river glideth at his own sweet will:
Dear God! the very houses seem asleep;
And all that mighty heart is lying still!

WILLIAM WORDSWORTH

# The Seal

Throb, throb from the mixer
Spewing out concrete.
And at the heads of the cables
Stand the serpent-warders.
Sweating and straining,
Thrusting those cruel mouths to their prey.
Hark how the steel tongues hiss
As they stab.
The men sway under the effort,
And their eyes are bloodshot with the din,
The clatter that shatters the brain.
Throb, throb from the mixer
Spewing out concrete.

The crowd stands by
Watching the smoothers;
Fascinated by the flat, wet levels
Of newlaid cement,
See how those curdled lakes
Glisten under the sky,
Virginal.

Then the dusty air suddenly divides,
And a pigeon from a plane tree
Flutters down to bathe its wings in that mirage of water.

But deceived, and angry,
Bewildered by the din,
The throb, throb from the mixer
Spewing out concrete,
It backs upon its wing,
Threshes air, and is gone.

But there, in the deflowered bed,
Is the seal of its coral foot,
Set till rocks crumble.                    RICHARD CHURCH

# Snow in the Suburbs

Every branch big with it,
Bent every twig with it;
Every fork like a white web-foot;
Every street and pavement mute:
Some flakes have lost their way, and grope back upward, when
Meeting those meandering down they turn and descend again.
The palings are glued together like a wall,
And there is no waft of wind with the fleecy fall.

A sparrow enters the tree,
Whereon immediately
A snow-lump thrice his own slight size
Descends on him and showers his head and eyes.
And overturns him,
And near inurns him,
And lights on a nether twig, when its brush
Starts off a volley of other lodging lumps with a rush.

The steps are a blanched slope,
Up which, with feeble hope,
A black cat comes, wide-eyed and thin;
And we take him in.

THOMAS HARDY

# London Snow

When men were all asleep the snow came flying,
In large white flakes falling on the city brown,
Stealthily and perpetually settling and loosely lying,
Hushing the latest traffic of the drowsy town;
Deadening, muffling, stifling its murmurs failing;
Lazily and incessantly floating down and down:

93

Silently sifting and veiling road, roof and railing;
Hiding difference, making unevenness even,
Into angles and crevices softly drifting and sailing.
  All night it fell, and when full inches seven
It lay in the depth of its uncompacted lightness,
The clouds blew off from a high and frosty heaven;
  And all woke earlier for the unaccustomed brightness
Of the winter dawning, the strange unheavenly glare:
The eye marvelled – marvelled at the dazzling whiteness;
  The ear hearkened to the stillness of the solemn air;
No sound of wheel rumbling nor of foot falling,
And the busy morning cries came thin and spare,
  Then boys I heard, as they went to school, calling,
They gathered up the crystal manna to freeze
Their tongues with tasting, their hands with snowballing;
  Or rioted in a drift, plunging up to the knees;
Or peering up from under the white-mossed wonder,
'O look at the trees!' they cried, 'O look at the trees!'
  With lessened load a few carts creak and blunder,
Following along the white deserted way,
A country company long dispersed asunder:
  When now already the sun, in pale display
Standing by Paul's high dome, spread forth below
His sparkling beams, and awoke the stir of the day.
  For now doors open, and war is waged with the snow;
And trains of sombre men, past tale of number,
Tread long brown paths, as toward their toil they go;
  But even for them awhile no cares encumber
Their minds diverted; the daily word is unspoken,
The daily thoughts of labour and sorrow slumber
At the sight of the beauty that greets them, for the charm they
  have broken.

R. BRIDGES

# Morning Express

Along the wind-swept platform, pinched and white,
The travellers stand in pools of wintry light,
Offering themselves to morn's long slanting arrows.
The train's due; porters trundle laden barrows.
The train steams in, volleying resplendent clouds
Of sun-blown vapour. Hither and about,
Scared people hurry, storming the doors in crowds.
The officials seem to waken with a shout,
Resolved to hoist and plunder; some to the vans
Leap; others tumble the milk in gleaming cans.

Boys, indolent-eyed, from baskets leaning back,
Question each face; a man with a hammer steals
Stooping from coach to coach; with clang and clack,
Touches and tests, and listens to the wheels.
Guard sounds a warning whistle, points to the clock
With brandished flag, and on his folded flock
Claps the last door: the monster grunts: 'Enough!'
Tightening his load of links with pant and puff.
Under the arch, then forth into blue day
Glide the processional windows on their way,
And glimpse the stately folk who sit at ease
To view the world like kings taking the seas
In prosperous weather: drifting banners tell
Their progress to the counties; with them goes
The glamour of their journeying; while those
Who sped them stand to wave a last farewell.

SIEGFRIED SASSOON

# Creative Writing

1 Look again at the *Prelude* on p. 90. Write a second prelude of your own describing a different time of the day in the city.

2 Look carefully at the photograph on p. 89 which shows one of the largest cranes in the world; it can lift one hundred tons and reach out with the weight one hundred and twenty-two feet.

   Imagine you are either the crane-driver or a bystander and describe in a poem what you feel and what you see.

3 Write a poem about either a modern skyscraper building or an industrial area. If you choose the second, concentrate particularly on the *shapes* of factories, cooling towers, gas-holders, chimneys and similar features. The photograph on pp. 96 and 97 will help you.

4 Describe your town from a high vantage-point. You may be looking from a top-storey window, or on a hill overlooking the town; or even in an aeroplane. L. S. Lowry's picture on p. 91 might help you. What strikes you first when you look at the picture? What details do you notice about the street and its inhabitants? What impression do you get of the city in the background?

5 Imagine you are looking through one of those slits that builders leave in the wooden boards surrounding a building site. The builders are working on the foundations. Look at the general scene, then pick out any details that attract your attention — a yellow mechanical digger . . . a bulldozer . . . a cement-mixer . . . cables . . . trenches.

   Describe, in a poem, what you see.

# COUNTRYSIDE

## The Lonely Scarecrow

My poor old bones—I've only two—
A broomshank and a broken stave.
My ragged gloves are a disgrace.
My one peg-foot is in the grave.

I wear the labourer's old clothes:
Coat, shirt and trousers all undone.
I bear my cross upon a hill
In rain and shine, in snow and sun.

I cannot help the way I look.
My funny hat is full of hay.
—O, wild birds, come and nest in me!
Why do you always fly away?

JAMES KIRKUP

# Tall Nettles

Tall nettles cover up, as they have done
These many springs, the rusty harrow, the plough
Long worn out, and the roller made of stone:
Only the elm butt tops the nettles now.

This corner of the farmyard I like most:
As well as any bloom upon a flower
I like the dust on the nettles, never lost
Except to prove the sweetness of a shower.

EDWARD THOMAS

# Weathers

I

This is the weather the cuckoo likes,
    And so do I;
When showers betumble the chestnut spikes,
    And nestlings fly:
And the little brown nightingale bills his best,
And they sit outside at 'The Travellers' Rest,'
And maids come forth sprig-muslin drest,
And citizens dream of the south and west,
    And so do I.

II

This is the weather the shepherd shuns,
    And so do I;
When beeches drip in browns and duns,
    And thresh, and ply;
And hill-hid tides throb, throe on throe,
And meadow rivulets overflow,
And drops on gate-bars hang in a row,
And rooks in families homeward go,
    And so do I.

THOMAS HARDY

# Mid-Country Blow

All night and all day the wind roared in the trees,
Until I could think there were waves rolling high as my
    bedroom floor;
When I stood at the window, an elm bough swept to my
    knees;
The blue spruce lashed like a surf at the door.

The second dawn I would not have believed:
The oak stood with each leaf stiff as a bell.
When I looked at the altered scene, my eye was undeceived,
But my ear still kept the sound of the sea like a shell.

THEODORE ROETHKE


# Cows

In buttercup and daisy fields
The lowing cattle, white and brown,
Lie by the creamy hedge of may,
Or up to their shoulders stand
In waves of clovered hay.

Under the pasture's trees that grow
Out of their own dark pools of green
They gather in the evening's pale
Summerhouse of sky and leaves,
And milk the shadows of the brindled vale.

JAMES KIRKUP

# An Autumn Morning

The autumn morning, waked by many a gun,
Throws o'er the fields her many-coloured light,
Wood wildly touched, close tanned, and stubbles dun,
A motley paradise for earth's delight;
Clouds ripple as the darkness breaks to light,
And clover plots are hid with silver mist,
One shower of cobwebs o'er the surface spread;
And threads of silk in strange disorder twist
Round every leaf and blossom's bottly head;
Hares in the drowning herbage scarcely steal
But on the battered pathway squat abed
And by the cart-rut nip their morning meal.
Look where we may, the scene is strange and new,
And every object wears a changing hue.

JOHN CLARE

# The Pettichap's Nest

Well! in my many walks I've rarely found
A place less likely for a bird to form
Its nest—close by the rut-gulled wagon-road,
And on the almost bare foot-trodden ground,
With scarce a clump of grass to keep it warm!
Where not a thistle spreads its spears abroad,
Or prickly bush, to shield it from harm's way;
And yet so snugly made, that none may spy
It out, save peradventure. You and I
Had surely passed it in our walk today,
Had chance not led us by it!—Nay, e'en now,
Had not the old bird heard us trampling by
And fluttered out, we had not seen it lie,
Brown as the roadway side. Small bits of hay
Plucked from the old propt haystack's pleachy brow,
And withered leaves, make up its outward wall,
Which from the gnarled oak-dotterel yearly fall,
And in the old hedge-bottom rot away.
Built like an oven, through a little hole,
Scarcely admitting e'en two fingers in,
Hard to discern, the birds snug entrance win.
'Tis lined with feathers warm as silken stole,
Softer than seats of down for painless ease,
And full of eggs scarce bigger even than peas!
Here's one most delicate, with spots as small
As dust and of a faint and pinky red.
We'll let them be, and safety guard them well;
For fear's rude paths around are thickly spread,
And they are left to many dangerous ways.
A green grasshopper's jump might break the shells,
Yet lowing oxen pass them morn and night,
And restless sheep around them hourly stray;
And no grass springs but hungry horses bite,
That trample past them twenty times a day.

Yet, like a miracle, in safety's lap
They still abide unhurt, and out of sight.
Stop! here's the bird—that woodman at the gap
Frightened him from the hedge: 'tis olive-green.
Well! I declare it is the pettichap!
Not bigger than the wren, and seldom seen.
I've often found her nest in chance's way,
When I in pathless woods did idly roam;
But never did I dream until today
A spot like this would be her chosen home.

JOHN CLARE

# Clearing at Dawn

The fields are chill, the sparse rain has stopped;
The colours of Spring teem on every side.
With leaping fish the blue pond is full;
With singing thrushes the green boughs droop.
The flowers of the field have dabbled their powdered cheeks;
The mountain grasses are bent level at the waist.
By the bamboo stream the last fragment of cloud
Blown by the wind slowly scatters away.

From the Chinese, by LI PO
(*Trans. Arthur Waley*)

# Winter the Huntsman

Through his iron glades
Rides Winter the Huntsman,
All colour fades
As his horn is heard sighing.

Far through the forest
His wild hooves crash and thunder
Till many a mighty branch
Is torn asunder.

And the red reynard creeps
To his hole near the river,
The copper leaves fall
And the bare trees shiver.

As night creeps from the ground,
Hides each tree from its brother,
And each dying sound
Reveals yet another.

Is it Winter the Huntsman
Who gallops through his iron glades,
Cracking his cruel whip
To the gathering shades?

OSBERT SITWELL

# Housing Scheme

All summer through
The field drank showers of larksong;
Offering in return
The hospitality of grasses,
And flowers kneedeep.

Over those wide acres
Trooped the plovers,
Mourning and lamenting as evening fell.
From the deep hedgerows
Where the foam of meadowsweet broke,
The rabbits and mice
Peeped out, and boldly sat in the sun.

But when the oaks were bronzing,
Steamrollers and brickcarts
Broke through the hedges.
The white-haired grasses, and the seedpods
Disappeared into the mud,
And the larks were silent, the plovers gone.

Then over the newlaid roads
And the open trenches of drains,
Rose a hoarding to face the highway,
'Build your house in the country.'
RICHARD CHURCH

# Creative Writing

1 Look at the photograph on p. 110 and try to imagine what it feels
  like to be in a storm in the country. First, ask yourself these questions
  and (quickly) jot down words, phrases, comparisons and descriptive
  details that they may suggest to you:
  How do you first sense that there is going to be a thunderstorm?
  What happens to the atmosphere?
  How does the sky begin to change?
  What happens to things around you?
  Now make notes about the storm itself. Try to find vivid phrases
  and comparisons to describe the thunder, lightning and rain.
  What happens to trees, flowers, animals, buildings?
  After the storm what effect does the sun have on the countryside?
  What do you see?
  What do you smell?
  Now you have some ideas in note form; your next job is to arrange
  them in the pattern you want. The main thing that your poem must
  do is to express clearly what you want to say: do not bother about
  finding rhymes, therefore, because you will find that the words
  which make rhymes do not always make sense—at least, not the
  sense you want.
  Your notes will be in three groups—before, during and after the
  storm. You could choose one of these or all of them as your raw
  material for a poem. Then decide which of your notes are vivid
  enough to go into your poem and leave out the rest.
  Now that you have selected from your notes those ideas you want
  to keep, decide in which order they should be placed. When you are
  writing your poem it is often a good idea to vary the length of the
  lines so that, for example, one *long* line may carry the sound of
  thunder; or a *short* one may create the effect of a sudden flash of
  lightning.
2 Imagine you are walking through a wood at night by yourself and,
  perhaps, you are a bit frightened. Write a poem to try and capture
  the atmosphere and your feelings.
3 On pp. 100 and 104 there are pictures of two country scenes.
  Choose one and concentrate hard on it until you imagine yourself
  actually *in* the landscape. What do you see? What do you hear?
  What do you feel? Quickly write down some notes—single words
  or phrases only. Perhaps you can use these as the basis for a poem.

# HUMOUR

## Mr. Kartoffel

Mr. Kartoffel's a whimsical man;
He drinks his beer from a watering-can,
And for no good reason that I can see
He fills his pockets with china tea.
He parts his hair with a knife and fork
And takes his ducks for a Sunday walk.
Says he, 'If my wife and I should choose
To wear our stockings outside our shoes,
Plant tulip-bulbs in the baby's pram
And eat tobacco instead of jam,
And fill the bath with cauliflowers,
That's nobody's business at all but ours.'
Says Mrs. K., 'I may choose to travel
With a sack of grass or a sack of gravel,
Or paint my toes, one black, one white,
Or sit on a bird's nest half the night—
But whatever I do that is rum or rare,
I rather think that it's my affair.
So fill up your pockets with stamps and string,
And let us be ready for anything!'
Says Mr. K. to his whimsical wife,
'How can we face the storms of life,
Unless we are ready for anything?
So if you've provided the stamps and the string,
Let us pump up the saddle and harness the horse
And fill him with carrots and custard and sauce,
Let us leap on him lightly and give him a shove
And it's over the sea and away, my love!'

JAMES REEVES

III

# The Tale of Custard the Dragon

Belinda lived in a little white house,
With a little black kitten and a little gray mouse,
And a little yellow dog and a little red wagon,
And a realio, trulio, little pet dragon.

Now the name of the little black kitten was Ink,
And the little gray mouse, she called her Blink,
And the little yellow dog was sharp as Mustard,
But the dragon was a coward, and she called him Custard.

Custard the dragon had big sharp teeth,
And spikes on top of him and scales underneath,
Mouth like a fireplace, chimney for a nose,
And realio, trulio daggers on his toes.

Belinda was as brave as a barrel full of bears,
And Ink and Blink chased lions down the stairs,
Mustard was as brave as a tiger in a rage,
But Custard cried for a nice safe cage.

Belinda tickled him, she tickled him unmerciful,
Ink, Blink and Mustard they rudely called him Percival,
They all sat laughing in the little red wagon
At the realio, trulio cowardly dragon.

Belinda giggled till she shook the house,
And Blink said Weeck! which is giggling for a mouse,
Ink and Mustard rudely asked his age,
When Custard cried for a nice safe cage.

Suddenly, suddenly they heard a nasty sound,
And Mustard growled, and they all looked around.
Meowch! cried Ink, and Ooh! cried Belinda,
For there was a pirate climbing in the winda.

Pistol in his left hand, pistol in his right,
And he held in his teeth a cutlass bright,
His beard was black, one leg was wood;
It was clear that the pirate meant no good.

Belinda paled, and she cried Help! Help!
But Mustard fled with a terrified yelp,
Ink trickled down to the bottom of the household,
And little mouse Blink strategically mouseholed.

But up jumped Custard, snorting like an engine,
Clashed his tail like irons in a dungeon,
With a clatter and a clank and a jangling squirm
He went at the pirate like a robin at a worm.

The pirate gaped at Belinda's dragon,
And gulped some grog from his pocket flagon,
He fired two bullets, but they didn't hit,
And Custard gobbled him, every bit.

Belinda embraced him, Mustard licked him,
No one mourned for his pirate victim.
Ink and Blink in glee did gyrate
Around the dragon that ate the pyrate.

Belinda still lives in her little white house,
With her little black kitten and her little gray mouse,
And her little yellow dog and her little red wagon,
And her realio, trulio little pet dragon.

Belinda is as brave as a barrel full of bears,
And Ink and Blink chase lions down the stairs.
Mustard is as brave as a tiger in a rage,
But Custard keeps crying for a nice safe cage.

OGDEN NASH

# Growltiger's Last Stand

Growltiger was a Bravo Cat, who travelled on a barge:
In fact he was the roughest cat that ever roamed at large.
From Gravesend up to Oxford he pursued his evil aims,
Rejoicing in his title of 'The Terror of the Thames'.

His manners and appearance did not calculate to please;
His coat was torn and seedy, he was baggy at the knees;
One ear was somewhat missing, no need to tell you why,
And he scowled upon a hostile world from one forbidding
eye.

The cottagers of Rotherhithe knew something of his fame;
At Hammersmith and Putney people shuddered at his name.
They would fortify the hen-house, lock up the silly goose,
When the rumour ran along the shore: GROWLTIGER'S ON
    THE LOOSE!

Woe to the weak canary, that fluttered from its cage;
Woe to the pampered Pekinese, that faced Growltiger's rage;
Woe to the bristly Bandicoot, that lurks on foreign ships,
And woe to any Cat with whom Growltiger came to grips!

But most to Cats of foreign race his hatred had been vowed;
To Cats of foreign name and race no quarter was allowed.
The Persian and the Siamese regarded him with fear—
Because it was a Siamese had mauled his missing ear.

Now on a peaceful summer night, all nature seemed at play,
The tender moon was shining bright, the barge at Molesey
lay.
All in the balmy moonlight it lay rocking on the tide—
And Growltiger was disposed to show his sentimental side.

His bucko mate, GRUMBUSKIN, long since had disappeared,
For to the Bell at Hampton he had gone to wet his beard;
And his bosun, TUMBLEBRUTUS, he too had stol'n away—
In the yard behind the Lion he was prowling for his prey.

In the forepeak of the vessel Growltiger sate alone,
Concentrating his attention on the Lady GRIDDLEBONE.
And his raffish crew were sleeping in their barrels and their
    bunks—
As the Siamese came creeping in their sampans and their junks.

Growltiger had no eye or ear for aught but Griddlebone,
And the Lady seemed enraptured by his manly baritone,
Disposed to relaxation, and awaiting no surprise—
But the moonlight shone reflected from a thousand bright
    blue eyes.

And closer still and closer the sampans circled round,
And yet from all the enemy there was not heard a sound.
The lovers sang their last duet, in danger of their lives—
For the foe was armed with toasting forks and cruel carving
    knives.

Then GILBERT gave the signal to his fierce Mongolian horde;
With a frightful burst of fireworks the Chinks they swarmed
    aboard.
Abandoning their sampans, and their pullaways and junks,
They battened down the hatches on the crew within their
    bunks.

Then Griddlebone she gave a screech, for she was badly
    skeered;
I am sorry to admit it, but she quickly disappeared.
She probably escaped with ease, I'm sure she was not
    drowned—
But a serried ring of flashing steel Growltiger did surround.

The ruthless foe pressed forward, in stubborn rank on rank;
Growltiger to his vast surprise was forced to walk the plank.
He who a hundred victims had driven to that drop,
At the end of all his crimes was forced to go ker-flip, ker-flop.

Oh there was joy in Wapping when the news flew through the
  land;
At Maidenhead and Henley there was dancing on the strand.
Rats were roasted whole at Brentford, and at Victoria Dock,
And a day of celebration was commanded in Bangkok.

T. S. ELIOT

# Macavity: The Mystery Cat

Macavity's a Mystery Cat: he's called the Hidden Paw—
For he's the master criminal who can defy the Law.
He's the bafflement of Scotland Yard, the Flying Squad's
  despair:
For when they reach the scene of crime—*Macavity's not there*!

Macavity, Macavity, there's no one like Macavity,
He's broken every human law, he breaks the law of gravity.
His powers of levitation would make a fakir stare,
And when you reach the scene of crime – *Macavity's not there*!
You may seek him in the basement, you may look up in the
  air—
But I tell you once and once again, *Macavity's not there*!

Macavity's a ginger cat, he's very tall and thin;
You would know him if you saw him, for his eyes are sunken
    in.
His brow is deeply lined with thought, his head is highly
    domed;
His coat is dusty from neglect, his whiskers are uncombed.
He sways his head from side to side, with movements like a
    snake;
And when you think he's half asleep, he's always wide awake.

Macavity, Macavity, there's no one like Macavity,
For he's a fiend in feline shape, a monster of depravity.
You may meet him in a by-street, you may see him in the
    square—
But when a crime's discovered, then *Macavity's not there*!

He's outwardly respectable. (They say he cheats at cards.)
And his footprints are not found in any file of Scotland Yard's.
And when the larder's looted, or the jewel-case is rifled,
Or when the milk is missing, or another Peke's been stifled,
Or the greenhouse glass is broken, and the trellis past repair—
Ay, there's the wonder of the thing! *Macavity's not there*!

And when the Foreign Office find a Treaty's gone astray,
Or the Admiralty lose some plans and drawings by the way,
There may be a scrap of paper in the hall or on the stair—
But it's useless to investigate—*Macavity's not there*!
And when the loss has been disclosed, the Secret Service say:
'It *must* have been Macavity!'—but he's a mile away.
You'll be sure to find him resting, or a-licking of his thumbs,
Or engaged in doing complicated long division sums.

Macavity, Macavity, there's no one like Macavity,
There never was a Cat of such deceitfulness and suavity.
He always has an alibi, and one or two to spare:

At whatever time the deed took place—MACAVITY WASN'T
THERE!
And they say that all the Cats whose wicked deeds are widely
known
(I might mention Mungojerrie, I might mention Griddlebone)
Are nothing more than agents for the Cat who all the time
Just controls their operations: the Napoleon of Crime!

T. S. ELIOT

# The Common Cormorant

The common cormorant or shag
Lays eggs inside a paper bag.
The reason you will see no doubt
It is to keep the lightning out.
But what these unobservant birds
Have never noticed is that herds
Of wandering bears may come with buns
And steal the bags to hold the crumbs.

ANON

# The Walrus and the Carpenter

The sun was shining on the sea,
Shining with all his might:
He did his very best to make
The billows smooth and bright—
And this was odd, because it was
The middle of the night.

The moon was shining sulkily,
Because she thought the sun
Had got no business to be there
After the day was done—
'It's very rude of him,' she said,
'To come and spoil the fun.'

The sea was wet as wet could be,
The sands were dry as dry.
You could not see a cloud, because
No cloud was in the sky:
No birds were flying overhead—
There were no birds to fly.

The Walrus and the Carpenter
Were walking close at hand;
They wept like anything to see
Such quantities of sand:
'If this were only cleared away,'
They said, 'it *would* be grand!'

'If seven maids with seven mops
Swept it for half a year.
Do you suppose,' the Walrus said,
'That they could get it clear?'
'I doubt it,' said the Carpenter,
And shed a bitter tear.

'O Oysters, come and walk with us!'
The Walrus did beseech.
'A pleasant walk, a pleasant talk,
Along the briny beach:
We cannot do with more than four,
To give a hand to each.'

The eldest Oyster looked at him,
But never a word he said:
The eldest Oyster winked his eye,
And shook his heavy head—
Meaning to say he did not choose
To leave the oyster-bed.

But four young Oysters hurried up,
All eager for the treat:
Their coats were brushed, their faces washed,
Their shoes were clean and neat—
And this was odd, because, you know,
They hadn't any feet.

Four other Oysters followed them,
And yet another four;
And thick and fast they came at last,
And more, and more, and more—
All hopping through the frothy waves,
And scrambling to the shore.

The Walrus and the Carpenter
Walked on a mile or so,
And then they rested on a rock
Conveniently low:
And all the little Oysters stood
And waited in a row.

'The time has come,' the Walrus said,
'To talk of many things:
Of shoes—and ships—and sealing-wax—
Of cabbages—and kings—
And why the sea is boiling hot—
And whether pigs have wings.'


'But, wait a bit,' the Oysters cried,
'Before we have our chat:
For some of us are out of breath,
And all of us are fat!'
'No hurry!' said the Carpenter.
They thanked him much for that.


'A loaf of bread,' the Walrus said,
'Is what we chiefly need:
Pepper and vinegar besides
Are very good indeed—
Now if you're ready, Oysters dear,
We can begin to feed.'


'But not on us!' the Oysters cried,
Turning a little blue.
'After such kindness that would be
A dismal thing to do!'
'The night is fine,' the Walrus said,
'Do you admire the view?


'It was so kind of you to come:
And you are very nice!'
The Carpenter said nothing but,
'Cut us another slice:
I wish you were not quite so deaf—
I've had to ask you twice!'

'It seems a shame,' the Walrus said,
'To play them such a trick,
After we've brought them out so far,
And made them trot so quick!'
The Carpenter said nothing but,
'The butter's spread too thick.'

'I weep for you,' the Walrus said,
'I deeply sympathise.'
With sobs and tears he sorted out
Those of the largest size,
Holding his pocket-handkerchief
Before his streaming eyes.

'O Oysters,' said the Carpenter,
'You've had a pleasant run!
Shall we be trotting home again?'
But answer there was none—
And this was scarcely odd, because
They'd eaten every one.

LEWIS CARROLL

# The Dong with a Luminous Nose

When awful darkness and silence reign
Over the great Gromboolian plain,
Through the long, long wintry nights;
When the angry breakers roar
As they beat on the rocky shore;
When Storm-clouds brood on the towering heights
Of the Hills of the Chankly Bore:

Then, through the vast and gloomy dark,
There moves what seems a fiery spark,
A lonely spark with silvery rays
Piercing the coal-black night,
A meteor strange and bright:
Hither and thither the vision strays,
A single lurid light.

Slowly it wanders,—pauses,—creeps,—
Anon it sparkles,—flashes and leaps;
And ever as onward it gleaming goes
A light on the Bong-tree stems it throws.
And those who watch at that midnight hour
From Hall or Terrace, or lofty Tower,
Cry, as the wild light passes along,—
'The Dong!—the Dong!
'The wandering Dong through the forest goes!
'The Dong! the Dong!
'The Dong with a luminous Nose!'

Long years ago
The Dong was happy and gay,
Till he fell in love with a Jumbly Girl
Who came to those shores one day.
For the Jumblies came in a Sieve, they did,—
Landing at eve near the Zemmery Fidd
Where the Oblong Oysters grow,
And the rocks are smooth and grey.
And all the woods and the valleys rang
With the Chorus they daily and nightly sang,—

*'Far and few, far and few,*
*Are the lands where the Jumblies live;*
*Their heads are green, and their hands are blue,*
*And they went to sea in a Sieve.'*

Happily, happily passed those days!
While the cheerful Jumblies stayed;
They danced in circlets all night long,
To the plaintive pipe of the lively Dong,
In moonlight, shine, or shade.
For day and night he was always there
By the side of the Jumbly Girl so fair,
With her sky-blue hands, and her sea-green hair,
Till the morning came of that hateful day
When the Jumblies sailed in their Sieve away,
And the Dong was left on the cruel shore—
Gazing—gazing for evermore,—
Ever keeping his weary eyes on
That pea-green sail on the far horizon,—
Singing the Jumbly Chorus still
As he sate all day on the grassy hill,—


*'Far and few, far and few,*
*Are the lands where the Jumblies live;*
*Their heads are green, and their hands are blue,*
*And they went to sea in a Sieve.'*


But when the sun was low in the West,
The Dong arose and said,—
'What little sense I once possessed
Has quite gone out of my head!'
And since that day he wanders still
By lake and forest, marsh and hill,
Singing – 'O somewhere, in valley or plain
Might I find my Jumbly Girl again!
For ever I'll seek by lake and shore
Till I find my Jumbly Girl once more!'

Playing a pipe with silvery squeaks,
Since then his Jumbly Girl he seeks,
And because by night he could not see,
He gathered the bark of the Twangum Tree
On the flowery plain that grows.
And he wove him a wondrous Nose,—
A Nose as strange as a Nose could be!
Of vast proportions and painted red,
And tied with cords to the back of his head.
—In a hollow rounded space it ended
With a luminous lamp within suspended
All fenced about
With a bandage stout
To prevent the wind from blowing it out;
And with holes all round to send the light,
In gleaming rays on the dismal night.


And now each night, and all night long,
Over those plains still roams the Dong;
And above the wail of the Chimp and Snipe
You may hear the squeak of his plaintive pipe
While ever he seeks, but seeks in vain
To meet with his Jumbly Girl again;
Lonely and wild—all night he goes,—
The Dong with a luminous Nose!
And all who watch at the midnight hour,
From Hall or Terrace, or lofty Tower,
Cry, as they trace the Meteor bright,
Moving along through the dreary night,—
   'This is the hour when forth he goes,
   The Dong with a luminous Nose!
   Yonder—over the plain he goes;
      He goes!
      He goes;
   The Dong with a Luminous Nose!'
EDWARD LEAR

# The Owl and the Pussy-Cat

The Owl and the Pussy-Cat went to sea
In a beautiful pea-green boat,
They took some honey, and plenty of money,
Wrapped up in a five-pound note.
The Owl looked up to the stars above,
And sang to a small guitar,
'O lovely Pussy! O Pussy, my love,
    What a beautiful Pussy you are,
        You are,
        You are!
    What a beautiful Pussy you are!'

Pussy said to the Owl, 'You elegant fowl!
How charmingly sweet you sing!
O let us be married! too long we have tarried,
But what shall we do for a ring?'
They sailed away for a year and a day,
To the land where the Bong-tree grows,
And there in a wood a Piggy-wig stood,
    With a ring at the end of his nose,
        His nose,
        His nose,
    With a ring at the end of his nose.

'Dear Pig, are you willing to sell for a shilling
Your ring?' Said the Piggy, 'I will.'
So they took it away, and were married next day
By the Turkey who lives on the hill.
They dined on mince, and slices of quince,
Which they ate with a runcible spoon;
And hand in hand, on the edge of the sand,
    They danced by the light of the moon,
        The moon,
        The moon,
    They danced by the light of the moon.

EDWARD LEAR

# Soldier Freddy

Soldier Freddy
   was never ready,
But! Soldier Neddy,
   unlike Freddy
Was *always* ready
   and steady,

That's why,
  When Soldier Neddy
Is-outside-Buckingham-Palace-on-guard-in-the pouring-
  wind-and-rain-
     being-steady-and-ready,
  Freddy-
    is home in beddy.

SPIKE MILLIGAN

127

# SEA

## Across the Estuary *part I*

The fog floats in with the tide and lies on the mosses,
Branching up the channels like the veins on an old man's hand.
The world of field and farm, the woods and the embankment,
Are blurred away like figures on a slate.
Here, under the canvas of the fog,
Is only sand, and the dead, purple turf,
And gulleys in the mud where now the water
Thrusts flabby fingers. The wild geese
Feed beneath the mist, grey and still as sheep,
And cormorants curl black question-marks
Above the threshold of the sea.
                              Here is the track:
The ruts of cartwheels filled with water, the dark
Brogs of broom. Unseen, a curlew calls—
A shadow slipping through the rippling mist;
Byzantine domes of foam sail up the gutters.
But now—where is the track? where are the ruts? The broom
Skulks back into the dark, and every footstep,
Dug deep in mud, draws water through the heels.
Each step goes wrong. Here, forward—deep, the sand
Shifts under foot like scree. Backward—deeper.
Stand still then—squids of sand
Wrap suckers round my feet. The tide
Tops the rim of the gulleys, and the mist
Tightens its cold, wet nets about my throat.

NORMAN NICHOLSON

Note:  In the days when the estuaries of Morecambe Bay and South Cumber-
land were crossed regularly by travellers on foot and by coach, the
guides marked the track by planting branches of broom in the sands.
This was called 'brogging the sands'.

# Full Fathom Five

Full fathom five thy father lies;
   Of his bones are coral made;
Those are pearls that were his eyes:
   Nothing of him that doth fade,
But doth suffer a sea-change
Into something rich and strange.
Sea-nymphs hourly ring his knell:
      Ding-dong.
   Hark! now I hear them—
    Ding-dong, bell!

*The Tempest, Act I, sc. ii*
W. SHAKESPEARE


# Drowning

Lord, Lord! methought, what pain it was to drown!
What dreadful noise of waters in mine ears!
What ugly sights of death within mine eyes!
Methought I saw a thousand fearful wrecks;
Ten thousand men that fishes gnaw'd upon;
Wedges of gold, great anchors, heaps of pearl,
Inestimable stones, unvalued jewels,
All scattered in the bottom of the sea:
Some lay in dead men's skulls; and in those holes
Where eyes did once inhabit, there were crept,
As 'twere in scorn of eyes, reflecting gems,
Which woo'd the slimy bottom of the deep,
And mock'd the dead bones that lay scattered by.

*Richard III, Act I, sc. iv*
W. SHAKESPEARE

# The Main-Deep

The long-·rolling,
Steady-póuring
Deep-trenchéd
Green billów:

  The wide-topped,
Unbróken,
Green-glacid,
Slow-sliding,

  Cold-flushing,
—On—on—on—
Chill-rushing,
  Hush-hushing,

... Hush–hushing ...
      JAMES STEPHENS


# Cargoes

Quinquireme of Nineveh from distant Ophir
Rowing home to haven in sunny Palestine,
    With a cargo of ivory,
    And apes and peacocks,
Sandalwood, cedarwood, and sweet white wine.

Stately Spanish galleon coming from the Isthmus,
Dipping through the Tropics by the palm-green shores,
    With a cargo of diamonds,
    Emeralds, amethysts,
Topazes, and cinnamon, and gold moidores.

Dirty British coaster with a salt-caked smoke stack
Butting through the Channel in the mad March days,
 With a cargo of Tyne coal,
 Road rail, pig-lead,
Firewood, iron-ware, and cheap tin trays.

      JOHN MASEFIELD

# The Shell

See what a lovely shell,
 Small and pure as a pearl,
Lying close to my foot,
Frail, but a work divine,
Made so fairily well
With delicate spire and whorl,
How exquisitely minute
A miracle of design!

What is it? a learned man
 Could give a clumsy name.
Let him name it who can,
The beauty would be the same.

The tiny cell is forlorn,
Void of the little living will
That made it stir on the shore.
Did he stand at the diamond door
Of his house in a rainbow frill?
Did he push, when he was uncurled,
A golden foot or a fairy horn
Thro' his dim water-world?

Slight, to be crushed with a tap
    Of my finger-nail on the sand,
Small, but a work divine,
    Frail, but of force to withstand,
Year upon year, the shock
        Of cataract seas that snap
        The three-decker's oaken spine
Athwart the ledges of rock,
    Here on the Breton strand!

LORD TENNYSON

# The Shell

And then I pressed the shell
Close to my ear,
And listened well.

And straightway, like a bell,
Came low and clear
The slow, sad murmur of far distant seas

Whipped by an icy breeze
Upon a shore
Wind-swept and desolate.

It was a sunless strand that never bore
The footprint of a man,
Nor felt the weight

Since time began
Of any human quality or stir,
Save what the dreary winds and waves incur.

And in the hush of waters was the sound
Of pebbles, rolling round;
For ever rolling, with a hollow sound:

And bubbling sea-weeds, as the waters go,
Swish to and fro
Their long, cold tentacles of slimy grey:

There was no day;
Nor ever came a night
Setting the stars alight

To wonder at the moon:
Was twilight only, and the frightened croon,
Smitten to whimpers, of the dreary wind

And waves that journeyed blind . . .
And then I loosed my ear—Oh, it was sweet
To hear a cart go jolting down the street.

JAMES STEPHENS

# Seaside Serenade

It begins when you smell a funny smell,
And it isn't vanilla or caramel,
And it isn't forget-me-nots or lilies,
Or new-mown hay, or daffy-down-dillies,
And it's not what the barber rubs on Father,
And it's awful, and yet you like it rather.

No, it's not what the barber rubs on Daddy,
It's more like an elderly finnan haddie,
Or, shall we say, an electric fan
Blowing over a sardine can.
It's as fishy as millions of fishy fishes,
In spite of which you find it delishes,
You could do with a second helping, please,
And that, my dears, is the ocean breeze.
And pretty soon you observe a pack
Of people reclining upon their back,
And another sight that is very common
Is people reclining upon their abdomen.
And now you lose the smell of the ocean
In the sweetish vapour of sunburn lotion,
And the sun itself seems paler and colder,
Compared to vermilion face and shoulder.
Athletic young men uncover their torso
In the virile way that maidens adore so,
While paunchy uncles, before they bathe them,
In voluminous beach robes modestly swathe them.
The beach is peppered with ladies who look
Like pictures out of a medical book.
Last, not least, consider the kiddies,
Chirping like crickets and katydiddies,
Splashing, squealing, slithering, crawling,
Cheerful, tearful, boisterous, bawling,
Kiddies in clamorous crowds that swarm
Heavily over your prostrate form,
Kiddies who bring, as a priceless cup,
Something dead that a wave washed up.
Oh, I must go down to the beach, my lass,
And step on a piece of broken glass.

OGDEN NASH

# The *Revenge*

At Florés in the Azores Sir Richard Grenville lay,
And a pinnace, like a fluttered bird, came flying from far away:
'Spanish ships of war at sea! we have sighted fifty-three!'
Then sware Lord Thomas Howard: "Fore God I am no
    coward;
But I cannot meet them here, for my ships are out of gear,
And the half my men are sick. I must fly, but follow quick.
We are six ships of the line; can we fight with fifty-three?'

Then spake Sir Richard Grenville: 'I know you are no coward;
You fly them for a moment to fight with them again.
But I've ninety men and more that are lying sick ashore.
I should count myself the coward if I left them, my Lord
    Howard,
To these Inquisition dogs and the devildoms of Spain.'

So Lord Howard passed away with five ships of war that day,
Till he melted like a cloud in the silent summer heaven;
But Sir Richard bore in hand all his sick men from the land
Very carefully and slow,
Men of Bideford in Devon,
And we laid them on the ballast down below;
For we brought them all aboard,
And they blest him in their pain, that they were not left to
    Spain,
To the thumbscrew and the stake, for the glory of the Lord.

He had only a hundred seamen to work the ship and to fight,
And he sailed away from Florés till the Spaniard came in sight,
With his huge sea-castles heaving upon the weather bow.
'Shall we fight or shall we fly?
Good Sir Richard, tell us now,
For to fight is but to die!
There'll be little of us left by the time this sun be set.'
And Sir Richard said again: 'We be all good English men.
Let us bang these dogs of Seville, the children of the devil,
For I never turned my back upon Don or devil yet.'

Sir Richard spoke and he laughed, and we roared a hurrah, and
   so
The little *Revenge* ran on sheer into the heart of the foe,
With her hundred fighters on deck, and her ninety sick below;
For half their fleet to the right and half to the left were seen,
And the little *Revenge* ran on through the long sea-lane
   between.

Thousands of their soldiers looked down from their decks and
   laughed,
Thousands of their seamen made mock at the mad little craft
Running on and on, till delayed
By their mountain-like *San Philip* that, of fifteen hundred tons,
And up-shadowing high above us with her yawning tiers of
   guns,
Took the breath from our sails, and we stayed.

And while now the great *San Philip* hung above us like a
   cloud
Whence the thunderbolt will fall
Long and loud,
Four galleons drew away
From the Spanish fleet that day,
And two upon the larboard and two upon the starboard lay,
And the battle thunder broke from them all.

But anon the great *San Philip*, she bethought herself and
  went,
Having that within her womb that had left her ill content;
And the rest they came aboard us, and they fought us hand to
  hand,
For a dozen times they came, with their pikes and musqueteers,
And a dozen times we shook 'em off as a dog that shakes his
  ears
When he leaps from the water to the land.


And the sun went down, and the stars came out far over the
  summer sea,
But never a moment ceased the fight of the one and the
  fifty-three.
Ship after ship, the whole night long, their high-built galleons
  came,
Ship after ship, the whole night long, with her battle-thunder
  and flame;
Ship after ship, the whole night long, drew back with her dead
  and her shame.
For some were sunk and many were shattered, and so could fight
  us no more—
God of battles, was ever a battle like this in the world before?


For he said, 'Fight on! Fight on!'
Though his vessel was all but a wreck;
And it chanced that, when half of the short summer night was
  gone,
With a grisly wound to be drest he had left the deck,
But a bullet struck him that was dressing it suddenly dead,
And himself he was wounded again in the side and the head,
And he said, 'Fight on! fight on!'

And the night went down and the sun smiled out far over the
summer sea,
And the Spanish fleet with broken sides lay around us all in a
ring;
But they dared not touch us again, for they feared that we still
could sting,
So they watched what the end would be.

And we had not fought them in vain,
But in perilous plight were we,
Seeing forty of our poor hundred were slain,
And half the rest of us maimed for life
In the crash of the cannonades and the desperate strife;
And the sick men down in the hold were most of them stark
and cold,
And the pikes were all broken or bent, and the powder was all
of it spent;
And the masts and the rigging were lying over the side;
But Sir Richard cried in his English pride,
'We have fought such a fight for a day and a night,
As may never be fought again!
We have won great glory, my men!
And a day less or more
At sea or ashore,
We die—does it matter when?
Sink me the ship, Master Gunner—sink her, split her in twain!
Fall into the hands of God, not into the hands of Spain!'

And the gunner said, 'Ay, Ay,' but the seamen made reply:
'We have children, we have wives,
And the Lord hath spared our lives.
We will make the Spaniard promise, if we yield, to let us go;
We shall live to fight again and to strike another blow.'
And the lion there lay dying, and they yielded to the foe.

And the stately Spanish men to their flagship bore him then,
Where they laid him by the mast, old Sir Richard caught at
    last,
And they praised him to his face with their courtly foreign
    grace;
But he rose upon their decks, and he cried:
'I have fought for Queen and Faith like a valiant man and true;
I have only done my duty as a man is bound to do;
With a joyful spirit I Sir Richard Grenville die!'
And he fell upon their decks, and he died.


And they stared at the dead that had been so valiant and true,
And had holden the power and glory of Spain so cheap
That he dared her with one little ship and his English few;
Was he devil or man? He was devil for aught they knew,
But they sank his body with honour down into the deep,
And they manned the *Revenge* with a swarthier alien crew,
And away she sailed with her loss and longed for her own;
When a wind from the lands they had ruined awoke from
    sleep,
And the water began to heave and the weather to moan,
And or ever that evening ended a great gale blew,
And a wave like the wave that is raised by an earthquake grew,
Till it smote on their hulls and their sails and their masts and
    their flags
And the whole sea plunged and fell on the shot-shattered navy
    of Spain,
And the little *Revenge* herself went down by the island crags
To be lost evermore in the main.

LORD TENNYSON

# Creative Writing

1 Think back to the last time you were at the seaside. Imagine you are beachcombing. Describe in a poem the things that you see washed up on the tide-line and the thoughts which go through your mind. Remember that your poem should not be just a list of objects but should describe them *in detail* and the way in which the sea has affected them.

2 Write a poem about one of the following: you will need to use comparisons here — pools in the rocks; sand-dunes; maps and charts; a lighthouse; breakwaters; watching the sea engulfing a sand-castle; sea-birds round a cliff; the pier or promenade; a crowded beach on Bank Holiday. If you choose the last idea, the picture on pp. 134 and 135 might help you.

3 Look again at John Masefield's *Cargoes* on p. 130. Write your own poem describing, each in a separate verse, two or three different ships or boats. Here are some suggestions: a submarine, a yacht, a speedboat, a canoe, a paddle steamer, a punt.

4 Look again at Tennyson's and James Stephens' poems about shells on pp. 131 and 132. Write your own poem on the same subject and try to include some of the small details of the markings, shapes and colours of the shells.

5 Read the two poems by Shakespeare on p. 129 which describe the world at the bottom of the ocean. Imagine you are skin-diving and looking down at the sea-bed. Write a poem describing what you see. You may find a sunken treasure ship, or a coral reef, or beautiful or frightening sea-creatures, or even bones. . . .

# PEOPLE

## Children's Party

May I join you in the doghouse, Rover?
I wish to retire till the party's over.
Since three o'clock I've done my best
To entertain each tiny guest;
My conscience now I've left behind me,
And if they want me, let them find me.
I blew their bubbles, I sailed their boats,
I kept them from each other's throats.
I told them tales of magic lands,
I took them out to wash their hands.
I sorted their rubbers and tied their laces,
I wiped their noses and dried their faces.
Of similarity there's lots
'Twixt tiny tots and Hottentots.
I've earned repose to heal the ravages
Of these angelic-looking savages.
Oh, progeny playing by itself
Is a lonely fascinating elf,
But progeny in roistering batches
Would drive Saint Francis from here to Natchez.
Shunned are the games a parent proposes;
They prefer to squirt each other with hoses,
Their playmates are their natural foemen
And they like to poke each other's abdomen.
Their joy needs another's woe to cushion it,
Say a puddle, and somebody littler to push in it.
They observe with glee the ballistic results
Of ice cream with spoons for catapults,

And inform the assembly with tears and glares
That everyone's presents are better than theirs.
Oh, little women and little men,
Someday I hope to love you again,
But not till after the party's over,
So give me the key to the doghouse, Rover.

OGDEN NASH

# Ozymandias

I met a traveller from an antique land
Who said: Two vast and trunkless legs of stone
Stand in the desert . . . Near them, on the sand,
Half sunk, a shattered visage lies, whose frown,
And wrinkled lip, and sneer of cold command,
Tell that its sculptor well those passions read
Which yet survive, stamped on these lifeless things,
The hand that mocked them, and the heart that fed:
And on the pedestal these words appear:
'My name is Ozymandias, king of kings:
Look on my works, ye Mighty, and despair!'
Nothing beside remains. Round the decay
Of that colossal wreck, boundless and bare
The lone and level sands stretch far away.

P. B. SHELLEY

# Childhood

I used to think that grown-up people chose
To have stiff backs and wrinkles round their nose,
And veins like small fat snakes on either hand,
On purpose to be grand.
Till through the banisters I watched one day
My great-aunt Etty's friend who was going away,
And how her onyx beads had come unstrung.
I saw her grope to find them as they rolled;
And then I knew that she was helplessly old,
As I was helplessly young.

FRANCES CORNFORD

# The Mad Woman

As well within her billowed skirts
Like a great ship with sails unfurled,
The mad woman goes gallantly
Upon the ridges of her world.

With eagle nose and wisps of gray
She strides upon the westward hills,
Swings her umbrella joyously
And waves it to the waving mills,

Talking and chuckling as she goes
Indifferent both to sun and rain,
With all that merry company,
The singing children of her brain.

L. A. G. STRONG

# Zeke

Gnarly and bent and deaf's a post
Pore ole Ezekiel Purvis
Goeth crippin' slowly up the 'ill
To the Commoonion Survis.

And tappy tappy up the haisle
Goeth stick and brassy ferrule:
And Passon 'ath to stoopy down
An' 'olley in ees yerole.

L. A. G. STRONG

# The Old Men Admiring
# Themselves in the Water

I heard the old, old men say,
'Everything alters,
And one by one we drop away.'
They had hands like claws, and their knees
Were twisted like the old thorn-trees
By the waters.
I heard the old, old men say,
'All that's beautiful drifts away
Like the waters.'

W. B. YEATS

# Seven Ages of Man

All the world's a stage,
And all the men and women merely players;
They have their exits and their entrances,
And one man in his time plays many parts,
His acts being seven ages. At first the infant,
Mewling◆ and puking in the nurse's arms:      *crying feebly*
And then the whining schoolboy, with his satchel
And shining morning face, creeping like snail
Unwillingly to school. And then the lover,
Sighing like furnace, with a woeful ballad
Made to his mistress' eyebrow. Then, a soldier,
Full of strange oaths, and bearded like the pard,◆    *leopard*
Jealous in honour, sudden and quick in quarrel,
Seeking the bubble reputation
Even in the cannon's mouth. And then, the justice,
In fair round belly, with good capon◆ lin'd,     *young chicken*
With eyes severe and beard of formal cut,
Full of wise saws,◆ and modern instances,      *sayings*
And so he plays his part. The sixth age shifts
Into the lean and slipper'd pantaloon,◆     *foolish old man*
With spectacles on nose, and pouch on side,
His youthful hose well sav'd, a world too wide
For his shrunk shank;◆ and his big manly voice,   *leg*
Turning again toward childish treble, pipes
And whistles in his sound. Last scene of all,
That ends this strange eventful history,
Is second childishness and mere oblivion;◆     *nothingness*
Sans◆ teeth, sans eyes, sans taste, sans every thing. *without*

*As You Like It, Act II, sc. vii*

**W. SHAKESPEARE**

# The Miller

THE MILLERE was a stout carl for the nones;
Full byg he was of brawn, and eek of bones.
That proved wel, for over al ther he cam,
At wrastlynge he wolde have alwey the ram.
He was short-sholdred, brood, a thikke knarre;
Ther was no dore that he nolde heve of harre,
Or breke it at a rennying with his heed.
His berd as any sowe or fox was reed,
And therto brood, as though it were a spade.
Upon the cop right of his nose he hade
A werte, and theron stood a toft of herys,
Reed as the brustles of a sowes erys;
His nosethirles blake were and wyde.
A swerd and bokeler bar he by his syde.
His mouth as greet was as a greet forneys.
He was a janglere and a goliardeys,
And that was moost of synne and harlotries.
Wel koude he stelen corn and tollen thries;
And yet he hadde a thombe of gold, pardee.
A whit cote and a blew hood wered he.
A baggepipe well koude he blowe and sowne,
And therwithal he broghte us out of towne.

from the *General Prologue* to the
*Canterbury Tales*
GEOFFREY CHAUCER

# The Miller

*A Literal Translation*

The miller was an exceedingly strong fellow;
He was very muscular and heavy-boned.
That was evident enough for wherever he went
He would always win the prize of a ram for wrestling.
He was a thickset, broad and sturdy fellow;
There was no door that he could not heave off its hinges,
Or break by running at it with his head.
His beard was red like the hairs of a sow or a fox,
And was also broad and shaped like a spade.
Right at the tip of his nose he had
A wart on which stood a tuft of hairs
Red as the bristles of a sow's ears;
His nostrils were black and wide.
He bore a sword and buckler at his side.
His mouth was as great as a furnace.
He was loud-mouthed and a coarse joker
And talked mostly about sin and wickedness.
He was good at stealing corn and at taking three times his legal
    payment;
And yet he was honest as millers go.
He wore a white coat and a blue hood.
He could perform well on the bagpipes
And he played us out of town.

# Creative Writing

1 Write a poem about a person in a particular job or situation. You can choose your own or use one of the following: a steeple-jack, a tramp, a beggar, a miner, a ballet-dancer, a clown. If you write about the clown the photograph on p. 149 may help you.

Whichever subject you choose, describe the person actually engaged in his or her occupation. How do you imagine he feels about his way of life?

2 Think about your family, parents or relations. Choose one person and try to describe not only his or her appearance but also personality. It may help you to think of members of the family doing things around the house: mother making cakes; wash-day; the family watching T.V.; the new baby; grandma knitting.

3 Look at the picture of the man feeding his horse on p. 146. What details do you notice about the man's face and clothing? Can you jot down words and phrases to describe the horse's blinkers and harness, its mane, the texture of the nose-bag and any other details that catch your eye? Perhaps you can write a poem from your notes.

4 Write about people in crowds—a football crowd, a cinema queue, a crowded bus, rush-hour in your town. In your poem try to create the atmosphere of the occasion.

5 The picture on p. 152 shows a nineteenth-century scientist who has placed a small bird inside a glass container and is performing an experiment on it with an air pump. If you look carefully at the faces of the people round the table you will notice that each has a different reaction to the experiment. What do their expressions tell you about their feelings? What might your *own* feelings be on such an occasion? Try to write a poem suggested by the picture.

# PLACES

## Adlestrop

Yes. I remember Adlestrop—
The name, because one afternoon
Of heat the express-train drew up there
Unwontedly. It was late June.

The steam hissed. Someone cleared his throat.
No one left and no one came
On the bare platform. What I saw
Was Adlestrop—only the name.

And willows, willow-herb, and grass,
And meadowsweet, and haycocks dry,
No whit less still and lonely fair
Than the high cloudlets in the sky.

And for that minute a blackbird sang
Close by, and round him, mistier,
Farther and farther, all the birds
Of Oxfordshire and Gloucestershire.

EDWARD THOMAS

# At the Edge of the Wood

First, boys out of school went out of their way home
To detonate the windows; at each smash
Piping with delight and skipping for fright
Of a ghost of the old man popping over his hedge,
Shrieking and nodding from the gate.
Then the game palled, since it was only breaking the
    silence.
The rain sluiced through the starred gaps,
Crept up walls into the brick; frost bit and
    munched;
Weeds craned in and leant on the doors.
Now it is a plot without trees let into the wood
Piled high with tangle and tousle
Buried parapets and roots picking at the last mortar
Though the chimney still stands sheathed in leaves
And you can see for the time being where in a nook
A briony burst its pot with a shower of roots
And back through the press of shrubs and stems
Deep-coils into the woods.

PETER REDGROVE

# Stopping by Woods on a Snowy Evening

Whose woods these are I think I know.
His house is in the village though;
He will not see me stopping here
To watch his woods fill up with snow.

My little horse must think it queer
To stop without a farmhouse near
Between the woods and frozen lake
The darkest evening of the year.

He gives his harness bells a shake
To ask if there is some mistake.
The only other sound's the sweep
Of easy wind and downy flake.

The woods are lovely, dark and deep,
But I have promises to keep,
And miles to go before I sleep,
And miles to go before I sleep.

ROBERT FROST

# The Way through the Woods

They shut the road through the woods
Seventy years ago.
Weather and rain have undone it again,
And now you would never know
There was once a road through the woods
Before they planted the trees.
It is underneath the coppice and heath
And the thin anemones.
Only the keeper sees
That, where the ring-dove broods,
And the badgers roll at ease,
There was once a road through the woods.

Yet, if you enter the woods
Of a summer evening late,
When the night-air cools on the trout-ringed pools
Where the otter whistles his mate,
(They fear not men in the woods,
Because they see so few)
You will hear the beat of a horse's feet,
And the swish of a skirt in the dew,
Steadily cantering through
The misty solitudes,
As though they perfectly knew
The old lost road through the woods. . . .
But there is no road through the woods.

RUDYARD KIPLING

157

# Child on top of a Greenhouse

The wind billowing out the seat of my britches,
My feet crackling splinters of glass and dried putty,
The half-grown chrysanthemums staring up like accusers,
Up through the streaked glass, flashing with sunlight,
A few white clouds all rushing eastward,
A line of elms plunging and tossing like horses,
And everyone, everyone pointing up and shouting!

THEODORE ROETHKE

# The Midnight Skaters

The hop-poles stand in cones,
    The icy pond lurks under,
The pole-tops steeple to the thrones
    Of stars, sound gulfs of wonder;
But not the tallest there, 'tis said,
Could fathom to this pond's black bed.

Then is not death at watch
    Within those secret waters?
What wants he but to catch
    Earth's heedless sons and daughters?
With but a crystal parapet
Between, he has his engines set.

Then on, blood shouts, on, on,
    Twirl, wheel and whip above him,
Dance on this ball-floor thin and wan,
    Use him as though you love him;
Court him, elude him, reel and pass,
And let him hate you through the glass.

EDMUND BLUNDEN

# The Big Rock Candy Mountains

One evenin' as the sun went down
And the jungle fire was burnin',
Down the track came a hobo hikin',
And he said: 'Boys, I'm not turnin',
I'm headed fer a land that's far away
Beside the crystal fountains,
So come with me, we'll all go see
The Big Rock Candy Mountains.'

In the Big Rock Candy Mountains,
There's a land that's fair and bright,
Where the handouts grow on bushes,
And you sleep out every night.
Where the boxcars are all empty,
And the sun shines every day
On the birds and the bees and the cigarette trees,
And the lemonade springs where the bluebird sings,
In the Big Rock Candy Mountains.

In the Big Rock Candy Mountains,
All the cops have wooden legs,
The bulldogs all have rubber teeth,
And the hens lay soft-boiled eggs,
The farmer's trees are full of fruit,
And the barns are full of hay.
Oh, I'm bound to go where there ain't no snow,
Where the rain don't pour, the wind don't blow,
In the Big Rock Candy Mountains.

In the Big Rock Candy Mountains,
You never change your socks,
And the little streams of alcohol
Come tricklin' down the rocks.
There the brakemen have to tip their hats
And the railroad bulls are blind.
There's a lake of stew and of whisky too,
You can paddle all around 'em in a big canoe,
In the Big Rock Candy Mountains.

In the Big Rock Candy Mountains,
All the jails are made of tin,
And you can bust right out again
As soon as you are in.
There ain't no short-handled shovels,
No axes, saws or picks.
I'm goin' to stay where you sleep all day,
Where they hung the Turk that invented work,
In the Big Rock Candy Mountains.

# Creative Writing

1 Where do you go for your holidays? Which things do you remember most vividly? Describe them in a poem. The pictures on pp. 134 and 157 might help.

2 Read *Adlestrop* again on p. 154. This poem describes, amongst other things, something you will know well—the strange feeling of passing through an unknown place and the sight of the huge station sign-board spelling out its name. Write your own poem called 'Travelling'. You need not be on a train; you may be travelling by car or coach.

3 You are travelling by train and approaching a large city. Describe the gradual change from the open countryside to the busy city station. What things do you notice? In what order? Be careful to arrange your details properly.

4 Write a poem about one of the following places: a main-line station at night; an empty church; inside a theatre or cinema; a large supermarket; escalators in a big department store.

5 Read *The Big Rock Candy Mountains* on p. 159. Write a poem based on a similar idea—*your* idea of your own heaven.

6 The picture on p. 162 shows three parachutists in free fall. Imagine you are about to make a parachute jump from a 'plane. Describe, in a poem, your feelings beforehand, the sensation of falling, the landscape below you, and the last few seconds as the parachute floats you safely to earth.

# WITCHCRAFT, MAGIC and MYSTERY

---

## Now the Hungry Lion Roars

Now the hungry lion roars,
And the wolf behowls the moon;
Whilst the heavy ploughman snores,
All with weary task fordone.
Now the wasted brands do glow,
Whilst the screech-owl, screeching loud,
Puts the wretch that lies in woe
In remembrance of a shroud.
Now it is the time of night,
That the graves, all gaping wide,
Every one lets forth his sprite,
In the church-way paths to glide:
And we fairies, that do run
By the triple Hecate's team,
From the presence of the sun,
Following darkness like a dream,
Now are frolic; not a mouse
Shall disturb this hallow'd house:
I am sent with-broom before,
To sweep the dust behind the door.
*A Midsummer Night's Dream, Act V, sc. i*

W. SHAKESPEARE

163

# The Witches' Chant

*A Cavern: in the middle, a boiling cauldron.*
*Thunder.    Enter the three witches.*

| | |
|---|---|
| *1st Witch* | Thrice the brinded cat hath mew'd. |
| *2nd Witch* | Thrice, and once the hedge-pig whin'd. |
| *3rd Witch* | Harpier cries, ''Tis time, 'tis time.' |
| *1st Witch* | Round about the cauldron go: |
| | In the poisoned entrails throw; |
| | Toad, that under cold stone |
| | Days and nights has thirty one |
| | Swelter'd venom sleeping got, |
| | Boil thou first i' th' charmed pot. |
| *All* | Double, double, toil and trouble; |
| | Fire burn, and cauldron bubble. |
| *2nd Witch* | Fillet of a fenny snake, |
| | In the cauldron boil and bake; |
| | Eye of newt, and toe of frog, |
| | Wool of bat, and tongue of dog; |
| | Adder's fork, and blind-worm's sting, |
| | Lizard's leg, and howlet's wing; |
| | For a charm of powerful trouble, |
| | Like a hell-broth, boil and bubble. |
| *All* | Double, double, toil and trouble, |
| | Fire burn, and cauldron bubble. |
| *3rd Witch* | Scale of dragon, tooth of wolf, |
| | Witches' mummy, maw, and gulf |
| | Of the ravin'd salt-sea shark; |
| | Root of hemlock, digg'd i' th' dark; |
| | Liver of blaspheming Jew, |
| | Gall of goat, and slips of yew, |
| | Sliver'd in the moon's eclipse; |
| | Nose of Turk, and Tartar's lips; |

Finger of birth-strangled babe,
Ditch-deliver'd by a drab,
Make the gruel thick and slab;
Add thereto a tiger's chaudron,
For the ingredients of our cauldron.
*All*    Double, double, toil and trouble,
Fire burn, and cauldron bubble.

*Macbeth, Act IV, sc. i*
W. SHAKESPEARE

# Charm

The owl is abroad, the bat, and the toad,
And so is the cat-a-mountain;
The ant and the mole sit both in a hole,
And frog peeps out o' the fountain.
The dogs they do bay, and the timbrels play,
The spindle is now a-turning;
The moon it is red, and the stars are fled,
But all the sky is a-burning:
The ditch is made, and our nails the spade,
With pictures full, of wax and of wool;
Their livers I stick with needles quick;
There lacks but the blood to make up the flood.
Quickly, dame, then, bring your part in!
Spur, spur, upon little Martin,
Merrily, merrily, make him sail,
A worm in his mouth and a thorn in his tail,
Fire above, and fire below,
With a whip in your hand, to make him go!

BEN JONSON

# Welsh Incident

'But that was nothing to what things came out
From the sea-caves of Criccieth yonder.'
'What were they? Mermaids? dragons? ghosts?'
'Nothing at all of any things like that.'
'What were they, then?'
                    'All sorts of queer things,
Things never seen or heard or written about,
Very strange, un-Welsh, utterly peculiar
Things. Oh, solid enough they seemed to touch,
Had anyone dared it. Marvellous creation,
All various shapes and sizes and no sizes,
All new, each perfectly unlike his neighbour,
Though all came moving slowly out together.'
'Describe just one of them.'
                    'I am unable.'
'What were their colours?'
                    'Mostly nameless colours,
Colours you'd like to see; but one was puce
Or perhaps more like crimson, but not purplish.
Some had no colour.'
                'Tell me, had they legs?'
'Not a leg nor foot among them that I saw.'
'But did these things come out in any order?
What o'clock was it? What was the day of the week?
Who else was present? How was the weather?'
'I was coming to that. It was half-past three
On Easter Tuesday last. The sun was shining.
The Harlech Silver Band played *Marchog Jesu*
On thirty-seven shimmering instruments,
Collecting for Carnarvon's (Fever) Hospital Fund.
The populations of Pwllheli, Criccieth,
Portmadoc, Borth, Tremadoc, Penrhyndeudraeth,
Were all assembled. Criccieth's mayor addressed them

First in good Welsh and then in fluent English,
Twisting his fingers in his chain of office,
Welcoming the things. They came out on the sand,
Not keeping time to the band, moving seaward
Silently at a snail's pace. But at last
The most odd, indescribable thing of all,
Which hardly one man there could see for wonder,
Did something recognizably a something.'
'Well, what?'
               'It made a noise.'
                              'A frightening noise?'
'No, no.'
          'A musical noise? A noise of scuffling?'
'No, but a very loud, respectable noise—
Like groaning to oneself on Sunday morning
In Chapel, close before the second psalm.'
'What did the mayor do?'
                    'I was coming to that.'
                        R.GRAVES

# The Listeners

'Is there anybody there?' said the Traveller,
Knocking on the moonlit door;
And his horse in the silence champed the grasses
Of the forest's ferny floor:
And a bird flew up out of the turret,
Above the Traveller's head:
And he smote upon the door again a second time;
'Is there anybody there?' he said.

But no one descended to the Traveller;
No head from the leaf-fringed sill
Leaned over and looked into his grey eyes,
Where he stood perplexed and still.
But only a host of phantom listeners
That dwelt in the lone house then
Stood listening in the quiet of the moonlight
To that voice from the world of men:
Stood thronging the faint moonbeams on the dark stair,
That goes down to the empty hall,
Hearkening in an air stirred and shaken
By the lonely Traveller's call.
And he felt in his heart their strangeness,
Their stillness answering his cry,
While his horse moved, cropping the dark turf,
'Neath the starred and leafy sky;
For he suddenly smote on the door, even
Louder, and lifted his head:
'Tell them I came, and no one answered,
That I kept my word,' he said.
Never the least stir made the listeners,
Though every word he spake
Fell echoing through the shadowiness of the still house
From the one man left awake:
Ay, they heard his foot upon the stirrup,
And the sound of iron on stone,
And how the silence surged softly backward,
When the plunging hoofs were gone.

WALTER DE LA MARE

# Flannan Isle

'Though three men dwell on Flannan Isle
To keep the lamp alight,
As we steer'd under the lee, we caught
No glimmer through the night.'

A passing ship at dawn had brought
The news; and quickly we set sail,
To find out what strange thing might ail
The keepers of the deep-sea light.

The winter day broke blue and bright,
With glancing sun and glancing spray,
As o'er the swell our boat made way,
As gallant as a gull in flight.

But, as we near'd the lonely Isle,
And looked up at the naked height;
And saw the lighthouse towering white,
With blinded lantern, that all night
Had never shot a spark
Of comfort through the dark,
So ghostly in the cold sunlight
It seem'd, that we were struck the while
With wonder all too deep for words.

And, as into the tiny creek
We stole beneath the hanging crag,
We saw three queer, black, ugly birds—
Too big, by far, in my belief,
For guillemot or shag—
Like seamen sitting bolt-upright
Upon a half-tide reef:
But, as we near'd, they plunged from sight,
Without a sound, or spurt of white.

And still too mazed to speak,
We landed; and made fast the boat;
And climb'd the track in single file,
Each wishing he was safe afloat,
On any sea, however far,
So it be far from Flannan Isle:
And still we seem'd to climb, and climb,
As though we'd lost all count of time,
And so must climb for evermore.
Yet, all too soon, we reached the door—
The black, sun-blister'd lighthouse-door,
That gaped for us ajar.

As, on the threshold, for a spell,
We paused, we seem'd to breathe the smell
Of limewash and of tar,
Familiar as our daily breath,
As though 'twere some strange scent of death:
And so, yet wondering, side by side,
We stood a moment, still tongue-tied:
And each with black foreboding eyed
The door, ere we should fling it wide,
To leave the sunlight for the gloom:
Till, plucking courage up, at last,
Hard on each other's heels we pass'd
Into the living-room.

Yet, as we crowded through the door,
We only saw a table, spread
For dinner, meat and cheese and bread;
But all untouch'd; and no one there:
As though, when they sat down to eat,
Ere they could even taste,
Alarm had come; and they in haste
Had risen and left the bread and meat:
For at the table-head a chair

Lay tumbled on the floor.
We listen'd; but we only heard
The feeble chirping of a bird
That starved upon its perch:
And, listening still, without a word,
We set about our hopeless search.

We hunted high, we hunted low,
And soon ransack'd the empty house;
Then o'er the Island, to and fro,
We ranged, to listen and to look
In every cranny, cleft or nook
That might have hid a bird or mouse:
But, though we search'd from shore to shore,
We found no sign in any place:
And soon again stood face to face
Before the gaping door:
And stole into the room once more
As frighten'd children steal.

Aye: though we hunted high and low,
And hunted everywhere,
Of the three men's fate we found no trace
Of any kind in any place,
But a door ajar, and an untouch'd meal,
And an overtoppled chair.

And, as we listen'd in the gloom
Of that forsaken living-room—
A chill clutch on our breath—
We thought how ill-chance came to all
Who kept the Flannan Light;
And how the rock had been the death
Of many a likely lad:
How six had come to a sudden end,
And three had gone stark mad:

And one whom we'd all known as friend
Had leapt from the lantern one still night,
And fallen dead by the lighthouse wall:
And long we thought
On the three we sought,
And of what might yet befall.

Like curs a glance has brought to heel,
We listen'd, flinching there:
And look'd, and look'd, on the untouch'd meal
And the overtoppled chair.

We seem'd to stand for an endless while,
Though still no word was said,
Three men alive on Flannan Isle,
Who thought on three men dead.

WILFRID WILSON GIBSON

# Night Crow

When I saw that clumsy crow
Flap from a wasted tree,
A shape in the mind rose up:
Over the gulfs of dream
Flew a tremendous bird
Further and further away
Into a moonless black,
Deep in the brain, far back.

THEODORE ROETHKE

# Fairies' Song

*The fairies sing*
You spotted snakes with double tongue,
Thorny hedgehogs, be not seen;
Newts and blind-worms do no wrong,
Come not near our fairy queen.

Philomel, with melody,
Sing in our sweet lullaby,
Lulla, lulla, lullaby; lulla, lulla, lullaby:
   Never harm
   Nor spell, nor charm,
Come our lovely lady nigh;
So good night, with lullaby.

*First Fairy*
Weaving spiders come not here;
Hence, you long-legg'd spinners, hence!
Beetles black approach not near;
Worm nor snail do no offence.

*Chorus*
Philomel, with melody, etc.

*Second Fairy*
Hence, away! now all is well:
One aloof stand sentinel. *(Exeunt fairies. Titania sleeps)*

*A Midsummer Night's Dream, Act II sc. ii*
W. SHAKESPEARE

# The Knowledgeable Child

I always see—I don't know why—
If any person's going to die.

That's why nobody talks to me.
There was a man who came to tea,

And when I saw that he would die
I went to him and said 'Good-bye,

I shall not see you any more.'
He died that evening. Then, next door,

They had a little girl: she died
Nearly as quick, and Mummy cried

And cried, and ever since that day
She's made me promise not to say.

But folks are still afraid of me,
And, where they've children, nobody

Will let me next or nigh to them
For fear I'll say good-bye to them.

L. A. G. STRONG

# Creative Writing

1 If you have ever been to a fair you may have had a ride on the ghost-train. Write a poem about the journey!

2 Using Shakespeare's poem from *Macbeth* on p. 164 as a model, write a witches' chant of your own.

3 You may have read Lewis Carroll's *Alice in Wonderland* or C. S. Lewis's *Narnia* stories. In these books people enter strange worlds in unexpected ways. Imagine you are looking at a picture that you know well—maybe one you see each day at home or school. Suddenly you find you are falling into the world of the picture. What is it like? Where are you?

4 You wake up in the middle of the night. Your bedroom seems full of weird shapes and shadows. In the silence you hear a creaking noise. You are a bit frightened. Write a poem expressing your feelings.

# Index of First Lines

Above the quiet dock in midnight                             20
Ah, you should see Cynddylan on a tractor                     9
A lightning flash                                             3
All day—when early morning shone                             71
All night and all day the wind roared in the trees          103
All summer through                                          108
All the world's a stage                                     148
Along the wind-swept platform, pinched and white             95
Although the snow still lingers                              26
A man whose name was Johnny Sands                            40
And then I pressed the shell                                132
As I walked out in the streets of Laredo                     45
As I was walking all alone                                   15
As well within her billowed skirts                          145
At evening, sitting on this terrace                          69
At Florés in the Azores Sir Richard Grenville lay           137
A touch of cold in the autumn night                          29
A trout leaps high                                           26
At the butterflies                                            3
At the top of the house the apples are laid in rows          21
A widow bird sate mourning for her love                      23

Bang Bang Bang                                               50
Belinda lived in a little white house                       112
Blow the man down, bullies, blow the man down                44
Bright the full moon shines                                   2
But that was nothing to what things came out               166

Clusters of electric bulbs                                   88

Dawnlight opening                                            22

Earth has not anything to show more fair                     90
Elephants in the circus                                      23
Even the rainbow has a body                                  27
Every branch big with it                                     93

First, boys out of school went out of their way home        155
For me who go                                                 3
From troubles of the world                                   84
Full fathom five thy father lies                            129

Gnarly and bent and deaf's a post                           147
Growltiger was a Bravo Cat, who travelled on a barge        114

Harvest moon                                                 22
He clasps the crag with hookéd hands                         72

He hangs between his wings outspread 72
Here among long-discarded cassocks 81
How large unto the tiny fly 32

I always see—I don't know why— 174
I've just come from a place 4
I heard the old, old men say 147
I met a traveller from an antique land 144
In all this cool 20
In buttercup and daisy fields 103
In moving-slow he has no Peer 80
I sing of a maiden 43
Isled in the midnight air 77
'Is there anybody there?' said the Traveller 167
It begins when you smell a funny smell 133
It is a wonder foam is so beautiful 29
It looks like a man 5
'Twas on the shores that round our coast 65
'Twould ring the bells of Heaven 78
I used to think that grown-up people chose 145
I wish people, when you sit near them 27

John Gilpin was a citizen 56
Joseph was an old man 42

Leading me along 20
Lord, Lord! methought, what pain it was to drown! 129

Macavity's a Mystery Cat: he's called the Hidden Paw 116
May I join you in the doghouse, Rover 143
Morning haze 22
Mr Kartoffel's a whimsical man 111
My poor old bones—I've only two— 99

Now the hungry lion roars 163

On a withered branch 23
One evenin' as the sun went down 159
Over the land freckled with snow half-thawed 27
O where have you been, my long, long love 34

Quinquireme of Nineveh from distant Ophir 130

Seen from above 30
See what a lovely shell 131
Soldier Freddy 127
Strong-shouldered mole 80
Suddenly all the fountains in the park 28

Tall nettles cover up, as they have done 102
The autumn morning, waked by many a gun 104
The cat went here and there 74
The common cormorant or shag 118
The fields are chill, the sparse rain has stopped 106
The hop-poles stand in cones 158
The king sits in Dunfermline town 37
The long-rólling 130
The Millere was a stout carl for the nones 150
The moon on the pine 22
The Owl and the Pussy-cat went to sea 126
The owl is abroad, the bat, and the toad 165
The pure clean air came sweet to his lungs 46
There was an old farmer in Sussex did dwell 39
There was a weasel lived in the sun 83
There were three kings in the east 54
There were two sisters in a bower 13
These be 31
The summer river 23
The sun was shining on the sea 119
The wind billowing out the seat of my britches 158
The wind doth blow today, my love 36
The winter evening settles down 90
The winter trees like great sweep's brushes 29
They call me Hanging Johnny 41
They have the guise 26
They shut the road through the woods 156
They trapped her in the Indian hills 78
This is the weather the cuckoo likes 102
Though three men dwell on Flannan Isle 169
Throb, throb from the mixer 92
Thrice the brinded cat hath mew'd 164
Through his iron glades 107

Up the barley rows 5
Up to his shoulders 73

Well! in my many walks I've rarely found 105
When awful darkness and silence reign 122
When I saw that clumsy crow 172
When men were all asleep the snow came flying 93
When the tea is brought at five o'clock 76
Whose woods these are I think I know 155

Yes. I remember Adlestrop— 154
You spotted snakes with double tongue 173

# Index of Authors

Basho  22, 23
Betjeman, John  81
Blunden, Edmund  158
Bridges, Robert  93
Burns, Robert  54
Buson  3, 22

Carroll, Lewis  119
Chaucer, Geoffrey  150
Church, Richard  28, 92, 108
Clare, John  104, 105
Cornford, Frances  145
Cowper, William  56
Crapsey, A.  31

De la Mare, Walter  32, 77, 167
Drinkwater, J.  21
Dyment, Clifford  78

Eliot, T. S.  90, 114, 116
Endicoff, Max  88

Frost, Robert  155

Gibson, Wilfred Wilson  169
Gilbert, W. S.  65
Graves, R.  166

Hardy, Thomas  93, 102
Harvey, F. W.  84
Heath-Stubbs, John  50
Hodgson, Ralph  78
Hokushi  22
Hulme, T. E.  20, 29

Issa  3

Jonson, Ben  165
Joso  4

Kikaku  2
Kipling, Rudyard  156

Kirkup James  73, 103, 99

Lawrence, D. H.  23, 27, 29, 69
Lear, Edward  122, 126
Li Po (trans. Arthur Waley)  106

MacNeice, Louis  30
Masefield, John  46, 130
Milligan, Spike  127
Monro, Harold  76

Nash, Ogden  112, 133, 143
Nicholson, Norman  128

Onitsura  22, 26

Redgrove, Peter  155
Reeves, James  111
Rodgers, W. R.  28
Roethke, Theodore  80, 103, 158, 172
Ryota  26
Ryusui  20

Sassoon, Siegfried  95
Shakespeare, W.  129, 148, 163, 164,
    173
Shelley, P. B.  23, 144
Shiki  3, 5, 23
Sitwell, Osbert  107
Sodo  20
Sora  5
Stephens, James  130, 132
Strong, L. A. G.  29, 145, 147, 174

Tennyson, Lord  72, 131, 137
Thomas, Edward  27, 83, 102, 154
Thomas, R. S.  9

Wordsworth, William  90

Yeats, W. B.  74, 147
Young, Andrew  26, 71, 72, 80

# Sources and Acknowledgements

Thanks are due to the authors (or their executors), their representatives and publishers mentioned in the following list for their kind permission to reproduce copyright material:

L. A. G. Strong: 'Zeke', 'The Mad Woman', 'The Knowledgeable Child' and 'Winter' from *The Body's Imperfection*, Methuen & Co. Ltd.

Robert Frost: 'Stopping by the Woods on a Snowy Evening' from *The Complete Poems of Robert Frost*, Jonathan Cape Ltd., and Holt, Rinehart & Winston Inc., New York.

Algernon S. Crapsey: 'Cinquains' from *Verse* by Adelaide Crapsey, Alfred A. Knopf, Inc., New York.

Arthur Waley: 'Clearing at Dawn' from *Chinese Poems (trans.)*, Allen & Unwin Ltd.

John Heath-Stubbs: 'The History of the Flood' from *Selected Poems*, Oxford University Press.

Edward Thomas: 'Thaw' and 'The Gallows' from *Collected Poems*, and 'Tall Nettles' and 'Adlestrop' from *Selected Poems*, Faber & Faber Ltd., and Mrs Myfanwy Thomas.

Edmund Blunden: 'The Midnight Skaters', A. D. Peters & Co.

James Kirkup: 'Cows' from *The Prodigal Son*, and 'The Bird Fancier' and 'The Lonely Scarecrow' from *Refusal to Conform*, Oxford University Press.

F. Cornford: 'Childhood' from *Collected Poems*, The Cresset Press.

Siegfried Sassoon: 'Morning Express' from *Collected Poems*, Faber & Faber Ltd.

Richard Church: 'Quiet', 'The Seal' and 'Housing Scheme' from *The Collected Poems of Richard Church*, William Heinemann Ltd.

D. H. Lawrence: 'Elephants in the Circus', 'Bat', 'Spray', 'Talk' and 'The Rainbow' from *The Complete Poems of D. H. Lawrence*, William Heinemann Ltd.

Walter de la Mare: 'The Fly', 'The Moth' and 'The Listeners' from *Collected Poems*, The Society of Authors, and the Literary Trustees of Walter de la Mare.

John Masefield: 'Cargoes' and an extract from 'Reynard the Fox', The Society of Authors.

Rudyard Kipling: 'The Way Through the Woods' from *Rewards and Fairies*, Macmillan & Co. Ltd., and Mrs George Bambridge.

W. B. Yeats: 'The Old Men Admiring Themselves in the Water' and 'The Cat and the Moon' from *Collected Poems of W. B. Yeats*, Macmillan & Co. Ltd., and Mr M. B. Yeats.

Robert Graves: 'Welsh Incident' from *Collected Poems 1965*, A. P. Watt Ltd.

James Reeves: 'Mr Kartoffel' from *Collected Poems*, William Heinemann Ltd.

Robert Bridges: 'London Snow' from *Shorter Poems of Robert Bridges*, The Clarendon Press, Oxford.

Peter Redgrove: 'At the Edge of the Wood' from *The Nature of Cold Weather and Other Poems*, Routledge & Kegan Paul Ltd.

T. E. Hulme: 'Above the Dock' and 'Autumn' from *Speculations*, Routledge & Kegan Paul Ltd.

Spike Milligan: 'Soldier Freddy' from *A Dustbin Full of Milligan*, Dennis Dobson, Publishers.

Harold Monro: 'Milk for the Cat', Gerald Duckworth & Co. Ltd.

Osbert Sitwell: 'Winter the Huntsman', Gerald Duckworth & Co. Ltd.

John Betjeman: 'Diary of a Church Mouse' from *Collected Poems*, John Murray (Publishers) Ltd.

R. S. Thomas: 'Cynddylan on a Tractor' from *Song at the Year's Turning*, Rupert Hart-Davis Ltd.

Andrew Young: 'Last Snow', 'Swallows', 'The Eagle' and 'A Dead Mole' from *Collected Poems*, Rupert Hart-Davis Ltd.

Louis MacNeice: 'Under the Mountain' from *Collected Poems*, Faber & Faber Ltd.

T. S. Eliot: 'Prelude I' from *Collected Poems*; 'MacCavity the Mystery Cat' and 'Growltiger's Last Stand' from *Old Possum's Book of Practical Cats*, Faber & Faber Ltd.

Norman Nicholson: 'Across the Estuary Part I' from *Selected Poems*, Faber & Faber Ltd.

J. Drinkwater: 'Moonlit Apples' from *The Collected Poems of John Drinkwater*, Sidgwick & Jackson Ltd.

F. W. Harvey: 'Ducks' from *Ducks and Other Poems by F. W. Harvey*, Sidgwick & Jackson Ltd.

Clifford Dyment: 'The Tigress' from *Poems 1935–48*, J. M. Dent & Sons Ltd.

Ogden Nash: 'Seaside Serenade', 'Custard the Dragon' and 'Children's Party' from *Family Reunion*, J. M. Dent & Sons Ltd., and Curtis Brown Ltd., New York.

W. R. Rodgers: 'The Fountains' from *Awake! and other Poems*, Martin Secker & Warburg Ltd.

Theodore Roethke: 'The Sloth', 'Mid-Country Blow', 'The Serpent', 'Child on Top of a Greenhouse' and 'Night Crow' from *Words for the Wind*, Martin Secker & Warburg Ltd.

H. G. Henderson (*trans.*): 'Bright the Full Moon', 'Summer Night', 'In the House', 'Parting', 'The Little Duck', 'In the Moonlight', 'The Barleyfield', 'Crow', 'The Harvest Moon', 'Haze', 'Spring', 'Heat', 'Dawn', 'The World Upside Down', 'Moon Magic', 'Coolness in Summer', 'Moon-Viewing' from *An Introduction to Haiku*, Doubleday & Co. Inc., New York.

Ralph Hodgson: 'The Bells of Heaven' from *Collected Poems*, Macmillan & Co. Ltd.

Thomas Hardy: 'Snow in the Suburbs' and 'Weathers' from *Collected Poems of Thomas Hardy*, Macmillan & Co. Ltd., and the Trustees of the Hardy Estate.

James Stephens: 'The Main-Deep' and 'The Shell' from *Collected Poems*, Macmillan & Co. Ltd., and Mrs Iris Wise.

Max Endicoff: 'The Excavation'. Every effort has been made to trace the copyright holder of this poem.

The Authors wish to thank the following for permission to reproduce photographs:

*The Daily Mail:* 'Driver Joseph Clarke feeding his horse, Captain' and 'Parachutists in free fall'.

*The Guardian:* 'Bradford, Manchester, from Ashton New Road.'

*Cammell Laird and Co. (Shipbuilders and Engineers) Ltd., Birkenhead:* 'Electric Monotower Crane.'

*Fox Photos Ltd.:* 'Lakeland in Blossom', 'Forked Lightning'.

*Magnum Photos:* 'Clown outside Big Top' by Bruce Davidson.

*The Victoria and Albert Museum:* 'The Great Wave' by Hokusai.

*The Feoffees of Chetham's Library Manchester and Mr. Neville Cooper:* 'The Ballad Monger.'

*The Sun Newspaper Ltd.:* 'Bank Holiday Beach, Blackpool.'

*Kunstindustrimuseet, Copenhagen:* 'Agriculture' by G. Arcimboldo.

*Philadelphia Museum of Art:* 'Three Fishes' by Liu Ts'ai.

*Collection of the National Palace Museum, Taipei, Taiwan, Republic of China:* 'Cat' by Li Ti.

*Dahelm Museum, Berlin and Herr W. Steinkopf:* 'Two Chained Monkeys' by Pieter Breughel the Elder.

*Salford Corporation and Mr. Neville Cooper:* 'View from the Window of the Royal Technical College, Salford' by L. S. Lowry.

*The Tate Gallery and The Medici Society Ltd.:* 'The Cornfield' by J. Nash.

*Ashmolean Museum, Oxford:* 'Early Morning' by Samuel Palmer.

*The Tate Gallery:* 'Experiment with Air Pump' by Joseph Wright of Derby.

We wish to thank our mother and our wives for the very considerable help they have given in the preparation of the typescript.

M.G.B.
P.B.

181

ISBN 0 340 05230 9

First published 1968
Second edition 1970: second impression 1971, third impression 1973

The English Universities Press Ltd
St Paul's House, Warwick Lane, London EC4P 4AH

Printed Offset Litho in Great Britain by Cox & Wyman Ltd,
London, Fakenham and Reading